O   TA   403.9   .M38

Materials science and engineering.

MATERIALS SCIENCE AND ENGINEERING:

Its Evolution, Practice and Prospects

Edited by
Morris Cohen

Contributions by

Melvin Kranzberg
Cyril Stanley Smith
Richard S. Claassen
Alan G. Chynoweth

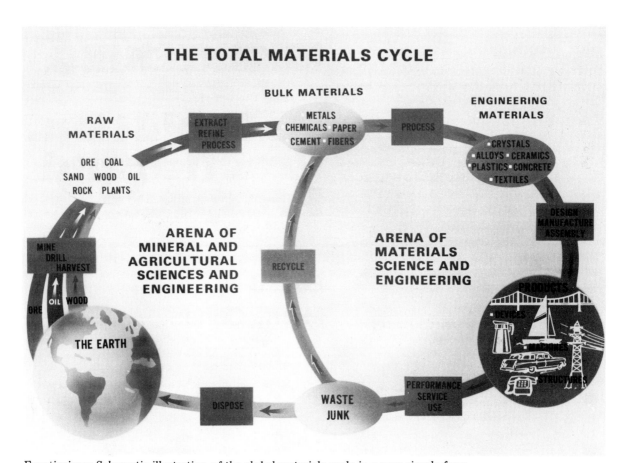

Frontispiece: *Schematic illustration of the global materials cycle in a very simple form.*

ACKNOWLEDGMENTS

This monograph is based on Volume I of the COSMAT Supplementary Report on "The History, Scope, and Nature of Materials Science and Engineering", published by the U. S. National Academy of Sciences in 1975. The authors are grateful to all who participated in the original study, and to the National Academy of Sciences (NAS) for permission to publish in this form.

An introduction to the overall COSMAT project, entitled "Materials and Man's Needs", is given in the Foreword. The COSMAT Steering Committee (with affiliations as of that time) consisted of:

*Morris Cohen (Chairman)	Massachusetts Institute of Technology
*William O. Baker (Vice Chairman)	Bell Telephone Laboratories, Inc.
Donald J. Blickwede	Bethlehem Steel Corporation
Raymond F. Boyer	Dow Chemical Company
*Paul F. Chenea	General Motors Corporation
Preston E. Cloud	University of California, Santa Barbara
*Daniel C. Drucker	University of Illinois
Julius J. Harwood	Ford Motor Company
I. Grant Hedrick	Grumman Aerospace Corporation
Walter R. Hibbard, Jr.	Owens-Corning Fiberglass Corporation
*John D. Hoffman	National Bureau of Standards
Melvin Kranzberg	Georgia Institute of Technology
*Hans H. Landsberg	Resources for the Future, Inc.
Humboldt W. Leverenz	RCA Laboratories, Inc.
Donald J. Lyman	University of Utah
Roger S. Porter	University of Massachusetts
Rustum Roy	Pennsylvania State University
*Roland W. Schmitt	General Electric Company
Abe Silverstein	Republic Steel Corporation
Lawrence H. Van Vlack	The University of Michigan

Ex-officio members

*Harvey Brooks (as former Chairman, Committee on Science and Public Policy, NAS)	Harvard University
*N. Bruce Hannay (as Chairman, National Materials Advisory Board, National Research Council)	Bell Telephone Laboratories, Inc.
*Ernst Weber (as Chairman, Division of Engineering, National Research Council)	National Academy of Sciences

Survey directors

Alan G. Chynoweth	Bell Telephone Laboratories, Inc.
S. Victor Radcliffe	Case Western Reserve University

*Members of COSMAT Executive Board.

TABLE OF CONTENTS

FOREWORD

COSMAT is the coined name given to a comprehensive study of the field of materials science and engineering, conducted during the early 1970's under the auspices of the U. S. National Academy of Sciences. The output has been published in five issues, bearing the general title "Materials and Man's Needs". These references are listed here to provide a more complete context for the present article:

Materials and Man's Needs
COSMAT Summary Report (1974), National Academy of Sciences, Washington, D. C. 20418
COSMAT Supplementary Report (1975), National Technical Information Service, Springfield, Virginia 22161
Volume I — The History, Scope, and Nature of Materials Science and Engineering
Volume II — The Needs, Priorities, and Opportunities for Materials Research
Volume III — The Institutional Framework for Materials Science and Engineering
Volume IV — Materials Technology Abroad

The two-part monograph being published here is based primarily on Volume I of the COSMAT Supplementary Report; Part I by Melvin Kranzberg and Cyril Smith corresponds to Chapter 1 on "Materials and Society" in Volume I, and Part II by Richard Claassen and Alan Chynoweth corresponds to Chapter 3 on "Materials Science and Engineering as a Multidiscipline" in Volume I.

Although the COSMAT inquiry attempted to view the materials field on a world basis, particularly through the operation of the global materials cycle (frontispiece), it is understandable that principal emphasis was placed on experience in the United States. For example, the case studies and most of the statistical data included in Part II clearly fall in this category. Nevertheless, readers from other countries will see substantial relevance for their purposes or, at least, obtain a good insight into the essential nature and modus operandi of materials science and engineering. As will be evident from the title of Volume IV above, COSMAT devoted considerable effort to examining materials technology in many countries, but inevitably the approach was motivated by seeking "lessons for the United States", and so was not intended to provide an integrated picture of the international materials field. Yet, for readers around-the-world, it may be helpful just to list the countries studied in various aspects: Canada, Czechoslovakia, Denmark, Finland, France, Germany, India, Japan, Korea, Norway, the Soviet Union, Sweden and the United Kingdom.

COSMAT adopted two key definitions:

(1) *Materials* are substances having properties which make them useful in machines, structures, devices and products. In other words, materials are the subset of matter in the universe that man uses for making things.

(2) *Materials science and engineering* (MSE) is concerned with the generation and application of knowledge relating the composition, structure

and processing of materials to their properties and uses. It should be noted that this definition refers to MSE in the singular; COSMAT found that, in an operational sense, MSE links science and engineering as a continuous field and, by its very nature, is not properly separable as such. Put in another way, MSE is the array of disciplines and subdisciplines that overlay the materials cycle.

The historical development of the interdependence between man and his materials is uniquely portrayed in Part I. We discover that materials have been ingrained in human culture since the beginning of history, and have now become the "working substance" of our civilization. Materials rank among the basic resources of society, along with food, energy, information, living space and manpower itself. Indeed, some of the strongest bonds that enter into mankind's partnership with nature lie in the realm of materials. It is no wonder, then, that intellectual and societal forces are tending to draw a science and engineering of materials (MSE) into being. Part II illuminates the scope, methodology and achievements of MSE.

MSE in its broadest sense is a multidiscipline, spanning many branches of knowledge that shed light on the field of materials. The disciplines thus involved continue to enjoy their separate identities within the total spectrum of human knowledge. MSE, however, forms a connective matrix which puts such disciplines into juxtaposition with one another so that basic understanding about materials can be transmitted through to eventual utilization by society. Countercurrently, the needs of society and experienced knowledge gained from the performance of materials in actual service are being transmitted back in the opposite direction. Thus, MSE provides a natural knowledge generation and conduction system in which the barriers that traditionally surround disciplines tend to dissolve under the intellectual stimulus to understand materials deeply, and under the societal driving force to use materials wisely.

It is easy to see that the very *multi*disciplinarity of MSE provides a fertile medium for the more tightly coupled *inter*disciplinary mode in which two or more disciplines are purposefully brought together to solve a perceived materials problem, *i.e.* to achieve an end-oriented materials advance in understanding or in development or in application. The case studies recounted in Part II offer enlightening examples of how MSE operates in its interdisciplinary mode.

In the perspective of Parts I and II, as distilled here so discerningly by the authors from the massive COSMAT survey, one can appreciate more clearly than ever a central point of the COSMAT message (Summary Report, 1974, p. xxiii): "Materials science and engineering is emerging, COSMAT believes, as a coherent doctrine or technical field with deep intellectual roots . . . It intimately combines knowledge of the condensed state of matter with the real world of material function and performance. It links the quest for deep fundamental study of matter with the imperative of satisfying man's needs."

MORRIS COHEN

*Massachusetts Institute of Technology,
Cambridge, Massachusetts, U.S.A.*

PART I
MATERIALS IN HISTORY AND SOCIETY

MELVIN KRANZBERG
Georgia Institute of Technology, Atlanta, Ga. (U.S.A.)
CYRIL STANLEY SMITH
Massachusetts Institute of Technology, Cambridge, Mass. (U.S.A.)

CHAPTER 1. INTRODUCTION

A Glimpse of the Materials Field

The field of materials is immense and diverse. Historically, it began with the emergence of man himself, and materials gave name to the ages of civilization. Today, the field logically encompasses the lonely prospector and the advanced instrumented search for oil; it spreads from the furious flame of the oxygen steelmaking furnace to the quiet cold electrodeposition of copper; from the massive rolling mill producing steel rails to the craftsman hammering out a piece of jewelry; from the smallest chip of an electronic device to the largest building made by man; from the common paper-bag to the titanium shell of a space ship; from the clearest glass to carbon black; from liquid mercury to the hardest diamond; from superconductors to insulators; from room-temperature-cast plastics to almost-infusible refractories; from milady's stocking to the militant's bomb; from the sweating blacksmith to the cloistered, contemplating scholar who once worried about the nature of matter and now tries to calculate the difference between materials.

One of the hallmarks of modern industrialized society is our increasing extravagance in the use of materials. We use more materials than ever before, and we use them up faster. Indeed, it has been postulated that, assuming current trends in world production and population growth, the materials requirements for the next decade and a half could equal all the materials used throughout history up to date [1]. This expanding use of materials is itself revolutionary and hence forms an integral part of the "materials revolution" of our times.

Not only are we consuming materials more rapidly, but we are using an increasing diversity of materials. Through most of history a few empirically selected abuse-tolerant general-purpose materials sufficed for the relatively untaxing applications that had been devised. Engineers accepted the limitation of available materials and designed in accordance with their known properties or small extensions of experience, while the producers of materials worked to balance reliability with cheapness rather than to achieve new properties. This has changed. A great range of new materials has opened up for the use of 20th century man: refractory metals, light alloys, plastics and synthetic fibers, for example. Some of these do better, or cheaper, what the older ones did; others have combinations of properties that enable entirely new devices to be made or quite new effects to be achieved. We now employ in industrial processes a majority of the ninety-two elements in the periodic table which are found in nature, whereas until a century ago, all but 20, if known at all, were curiosities of the chemistry laboratory [2]. Moreover, physical structure is even more important than chemical composition. Not only are more of nature's elements being put into service, but completely new materials are being synthesized in the laboratory. Our claim to a high level of materials civilization rests on this expanded, almost extravagant utilization of a rich diversity of materials.

This extravagance is both a product of advances in materials and a challenge to its future growth. The enlarged consumption of materials means that we shall have to cope increasingly with natural-resource and supply problems — and also with energy problems, for the extraction, processing, creation, or recycling of materials requires enormous consumption of increasingly scarce energy resources. Mankind is being forced, therefore, to enlarge its resource base by finding ways to employ existing raw materials more efficiently, to convert previously unusable substances to useful materials, to recycle waste materials and make them reusable, and to produce wholly new materials out of substances which are available in abundance.

A Glimpse of Materials Science and Engineering

The expanded demand for materials is not confined to sophisticated space ships or electronic and nuclear devices. In most American kitchens are new heat-shock-proof glasses and ceramics and long-life electric elements to heat them; the motors in electric appliances have so-called oilless bearings which actually hold a lifetime of oil, made possible by powder metallurgy; the pocket camera uses new compositions of coated optical glass; office copy machines depend on photoconductors; toy soldiers are formed out of plastics, not lead; boats are molded out of fiberglass; the humble garbage can sounds off with a plastic thud rather than a metallic clank; we sleep on synthetic foam mattresses and polyfiber pillows, instead of cotton and wool stuffing and feathers; we are scarcely aware of how many objects of everyday life have been transformed — and in most cases, improved — by the application of materials science and engineering (MSE). It is a new profession, an inseparable mixture of both science and engineering that is becoming known as MSE for short. Moreover, as with a rich vocabulary in literature, the flexibility that is engendered by MSE greatly increases the options in substitutions of one material for another.

Quite often the development of a new material or process will have effects far beyond what the originators expected. Materials have somewhat the quality of letters in the alphabet in that they can be used to compose many things larger than themselves: amber, gold, jewelry and iron ore inspired commerce and the discovery of many parts of the world; improvements in optical glass lay behind all the knowledge revealed by the microscope and telescope; conductors, insulators and semiconductors were needed to construct new communication systems which today affect the thought, work and play of everyone. Alloy steel permitted the development of the automobile; titanium the space program. The finding of a new material was essential for the

growth of the laser, the social uses of which cannot yet be fully imagined. In these, as in hundreds of other cases, the materials themselves are soon taken for granted, just as are the letters of a word. To be sure, the ultimate value of a material lies in what society chooses to do with whatever is made of it, but changes in the "smaller parts" reacting responsibly to larger movements and structures make it possible to evolve new patterns of social organization.

The transitions from, say, stone to bronze and from bronze to iron were revolutionary in impact, but they were relatively slow in terms of the time scale. Changes in materials innovation and application within the last half century, however, have occurred in a time span which was revolutionary rather than evolutionary.

The materials revolution of our times is qualitative as well as quantitative. It breeds the attitude of purposeful creativity rather than modification of natural materials, and also a new approach — an innovative organization of science and technology. The combination of these elements which constitutes MSE is characterized by a new language of science and engineering, by new tools for research, by a new approach to the structure and properties of materials of all kinds, by a new interdependence of scientific research and technical development, and by a new coupling of scientific endeavor with societal needs.

As a field, MSE is young. There is still no professional organization embodying all of its aspects, and there is even some disagreement as to what constitutes the field. One of the elements which is newest about it is the notion of purposive creation. However, MSE is responsive as well as creative. Not only does it create new materials, sometimes before their possible uses are recognized, but it responds to new and different needs of our sophisticated and complex industrial society. In a sense, MSE is today's alchemy. Almost magically, it transmutes base materials, not into gold — although it can produce gold-looking substances — but into substances which are of greater use and benefit to mankind than this precious metal. MSE is directed toward the solution of problems of a scientific and technological nature bearing on the creation and development of materials for specific uses. This means that it couples scientific research with engineering applications of the end-product: one must speak of materials science and engineering as an "it" rather than "them".

Not only is MSE postulated on the linkage of science and technology, it draws together different fields within science and engineering. From technology MSE brings metallurgists, ceramists, electrical engineers, chemical engineers; from science it embraces physicists, inorganic chemists, organic chemists, crystallographers and various specialists within those major fields.

In its development MSE not only involved cooperation among different branches of science and engineering, but also collaboration among different kinds of organizations. Industrial corporations, governmental agencies and universities have worked together to shape the outlines and operations of this new "field".

In recent years there has been a marked increase in the liaison between industrial production and industrial research, and between research in industry and that in the universities. The researcher cannot ignore problems of production, and the producer knows that he can get from the scientist suggestions for new products and sometimes help for difficulties. It should be noticed that MSE has come about by the aggregation of several different specialties that were earlier separate, not as so often happens by growth of increased diversity within a field which keeps some cohesion. This change is just as much on the industrial side as it is on the academic. Industry continually uses its old production capabilities on new materials, and the scientist finds himself forced to look at a different scale of aggregation of matter.

Most of the work on materials until the 20th century was aimed at making the old materials available in greater quantity, of better quality, or at less cost. The new world in which materials are developed for specific purposes (usually by persons who are concerned with end-use rather than with the production of the materials themselves) introduces a fundamental change, indeed. Heretofore, engineers were limited in their designs to the use of materials already "on the shelf". This limitation no longer applies, and the design of new materials is becoming a very intimate part of almost every engineering plan. MSE interacts particularly well with engineers who have

some application in mind. It often reaches the general public through secondary effects, such as negatively via the pollution which results from mining, smelting, or processing operations, and positively via the taken-for-granted materials that underlie every product and service in today's complicated world. We clothe ourselves in materials of man-made fibers; we eat food from plastic containers; we drive cars made of a variety of "natural" and synthetic materials; and we watch TV on sets whose components possess special electronic properties.

The rising tide of "materials expectations" is not for the materials themselves, but for things which of necessity incorporate materials. That materials are secondary in most end-applications is obvious from the name applied to the materials that remain when a machine or structure no longer serves its purpose — "junk". There is, however, at least one positive direct contact, that of waste-material processing; city waste disposal is a very challenging materials-processing problem, especially if the entire cycle from production, use and reuse of materials can be brought into proper balance.

As one cynical observer put it, "For the first two decades of its existence, materials science and engineering was engaged in producing new and better products for mankind; its major task for the next two decades is to help us get rid of the rubbish accumulated because of the successes of the past twenty years".

CHAPTER 2. IMPORTANCE OF MATERIALS TO MAN

Matter versus *Materials*

Materials are so ubiquitous and so important to man's life and welfare that we must obviously delimit the term in this survey, lest we find ourselves investigating nearly every aspect of science and technology and describing virtually every facet of human existence and social life. Unless we limit our scope, all matter in the universe will inadvertently be encompassed within the scope of our subject.

But *matter* is not the same as *material*. Mainly we are concerned with materials that are to become part of a device or structure or product made by man. The science part of

MSE seeks to discover, analyze and understand the nature of materials, to provide coherent explanations of the origin of the properties that are used, while the engineering aspect takes this basic knowledge and whatever else is necessary (not the least of which is experience) to develop, prepare and apply materials for specified needs, often the most advanced objectives of the times. It is the necessarily intimate relationship between these disparate activities that, to some extent, distinguishes MSE from other fields and which makes it so fascinating for its practitioners. The benefits come not only from the production of age-old materials in greater quantities and with less cost — an aspect which has perhaps the most visible influence on the modern world — but it also involves the production of materials with totally new properties. Both of these contributions have changed the economy and social structure, and both have come about in large measure through the application of a mixture of theoretical and empirical science with entrepreneurship. And just as the development of mathematical principles of design enabled the 19th century engineer to test available materials and select the best suited for his constructions, so the deeper understanding of the structural basis of materials has given the scientist a viewpoint applicable to all materials, and at every stage from their manufacture to their societal use and ultimate return to earth.

Some Influences on Man's Environment and Attitudes

The production of materials has always been accompanied by some form of pollution, but this only became a problem when industrialization and population enormously increased the scale of operation. Longfellow's poem contains no complaint about the smoke arising from the village smithy's forge; if one of today's poets would attempt to glorify the blacksmith's modern counterpart, he would undoubtedly describe the smoke belching forth from the foundry, but there would be no mention of spreading chestnut trees because all those within a half-mile radius would long ago have withered from the pollution of the surrounding neighborhood. The simple fact is that an industrial civilization represents more activity, more production and usually more pollution, even though the pol-

lution attributable to each unit produced has been sharply decreased.

The utilization of materials, as well as their manufacture, also generates pollution. Those of us living in affluent highly industrialized countries enjoy the benefits of a "throwaway" society. The problem arises from the fact that many of the products we use are made from materials which are not strictly "throw-awayable." Natural processes do not readily return all materials to the overall cycle, and in the case of certain mineral products, we can sometimes find no better way of disposing of scrap than to bury it back in the earth from which we had originally extracted it at great trouble and expense. Proposals for reuse or recycling often founder upon public apathy — but this is changing and MSE has an important role to play.

The moral and spiritual impact of materials on both consumer and producer is both less visible and more debatable. To those reared in a Puritanical ethic of self-denial, the outpouring of materials goods would seem almost sinful, as would the waste products of a throwaway society. Such conspicuous consumption would seem almost immoral in a world where so many people are still lacking basic material essentials. A more sophisticated objection might be that the very profusion of materials presents modern man with psychological dilemmas. We are presented with so many options that we find it difficult to choose among them [3].

It might be surprising to some that the question of the debasement of the materials producer should even be raised. Scientists have long claimed that their pursuit of an understanding of nature is innocent, and technologists have always assumed that their gifts of materials plenty to mankind would be welcomed. Hence, it has come as a shock to them during the past few years that the benefits of science and technology have been questioned. Both science and technology have been subjected to criticism from highly articulate members of the literature subculture, as well as from within their own ranks, regarding their contributions to mankind's destructive activities and to the deterioration of the environment [4].

To those engaged in materials production and fabrication, it may be disconcerting to realize that for a fair fraction of human history their activities have been viewed with suspicion and downright distaste by social thinkers and by the general public. The ancient Greek philosophers, who set the tone for many of the attitudes still prevalent throughout Western Civilization, regarded those involved in the production of material goods as being less worthy than agriculturists and others who did not perform such mundane tasks. Greek mythology provided a basis for this disdain: the Greek gods were viewed as idealistic models of physical perfection; the only flawed immortal was the patron god of the metalworker, Hephaestus, whose lameness made him the butt of jokes among his Olympian colleagues. (But he got along well with Aphrodite, another producer!)

Throughout ancient society the most menial tasks, especially those of mining and metallurgy, were left to slaves. Hence, the common social attitude of antiquity, persisting to this day in some intellectual circles, was to look down upon those who worked with their hands. Xenophon [5] stated the case in this fashion, "What are called the mechanical arts carry a social stigma and are rightly dishonored in our cities. For these arts damage the bodies of those who work at them or who act as overseers, by compelling them to a sedentary life and to an indoor life, and, in some cases, to spend the whole day by the fire. This physical degeneration results also in deterioration of the soul. Furthermore, the workers at these trades simply have not got the time to perform the offices of friendship or citizenship. Consequently they are looked upon as bad friends and bad patriots, and in some cities, especially the warlike ones, it is not legal for a citizen to ply a mechanical trade."

The ancients appreciated material goods but they did not think highly of those who actually produced them. In his life of Marcellus, Plutarch delivered this critical judgement, "For it does not of necessity follow that, if the work delights you with its grace, the one who wrought it is worthy of esteem." The current apprehension concerning dangers to the environment from materials production might result in materials scientists and engineers being regarded with similar suspicion today.

But there is yet a subtler way in which the triumphs of MSE might threaten the spirit of Western man. Advances in materials have gone beyond the simple task of conquering nature and mastering the environment. MSE attempts to improve upon nature. In a sense, this represents the ancient Greek sin of *hubris*, inordinate pride, where men thought they could rival or even excel the gods — and retribution from the gods followed inevitably. This may also be "original sin", the Christian sin of pride, which caused Adam's fall. By eating the fruit of the tree of knowledge, Adam thought that he would know as much as God. Conceivably, by endeavoring to outdo nature modern man is preparing his own fall. Or perhaps his new knowledge will lead to control as well as power, and to a richer life for mankind.

CHAPTER 3. MATERIALS IN THE EVOLUTION OF MAN AND IN PREHISTORY

Materials in Human Evolution

The very essence of a cultural development is its interrelatedness. This survey places emphasis on materials, but it should be obvious that materials *per se* are of little value unless they are shaped into a form that permits man to make or do something useful, or one that he finds delightful to touch or to contemplate. The material simply permits things to be done because of its bulk, its strength or, in more recent times, its varied combinations of physical, chemical and mechanical properties. The internal structure of the material that gives these properties is simply one stage in the complex hierarchy of physical and conceptual structures that make up the totality of man's works and aspirations.

We do not know exactly when our present human species *homo sapiens* came into being, but we do know that materials must have played a part in the evolution of man from more primitive forms of animal primates. It was the interaction of biological material and cultural processes that differentiated man from the rest of the animal world [6]. Other animals possess great physical advantages over man: the lion is stronger, the horse is faster, the giraffe has a greater reach for food. Nevertheless, man possesses certain anatomical features which proved particularly useful in enabling him to deal with his environment [7].

Modern physical anthropologists believe that there is a direct connection between such cultural traits as toolmaking and tool-using, and the development of man's physical characteristics, including his brain and his hand [8]. Man would not have become Man the Thinker (*homo sapiens*) had he not at the same time been Man the Maker (*homo faber*). Man made tools, but tools also made man. Perhaps man did not throw stones because he was standing up; he could have learned to stand erect the better to throw stones.

It is probable that the earliest humans used tools rather than made them, *i.e.* they selected whatever natural objects were at hand for immediate use before they anticipated a possible future task and prepared the tools for it. Once this idea was formulated and man began to discover and test out things for what they could do, he found natural objects — sticks, fibers, hides — and combined materials and shapes to serve his purposes. He tried bones and horn, but the hardest and densest material at hand was stone. When he further learned how to form materials as well as select them, and to communicate his knowledge, civilization could begin; it appears there was a strong evolutionary bias towards anatomical and mental types that could do this. While the early stages still remain the realm of hypothesis, there is general agreement that it was over two million years ago when a pre-human hominid began to use pebbles or stones as tools, though the shaping of specialized tools came slowly.

Materials in Cultural and Social Development

The recognition that there had been a cultural level to which we now give the name of Stone Age — itself a tribute to the importance of materials in man's development — did not occur until well into the 19th century. When, in about 1837, the Frenchman Boucher de Perthes propounded the view that some oddly shaped stones were not "freaks of nature" but were the result of directed purposeful work by human hands, he was ridiculed. Only when the vastness of geological time scales was established and it became possible to depart from a literal interpretation of biblical Genesis could credence be given to the notion that these stones were actually tools [9].

Some of the features of today's materials engineering can already be seen in the selection of flint by our prehistoric forebears as the best material for making tools and weapons. Availability, shapability and serviceability are balanced. The brittleness of flint enabled it to be chipped and flaked into specialized tools, but it was not too fragile for service in the form of scrapers, knives, awls, hand axes and the like. The geopolitical importance of material sources also appears early. It is perhaps not surprising that we find the most advanced early technologies and societies developing where good-quality flint was available. It may even be, as Jacobs has surmised [10], that cities arose from centers for trading flint (and perhaps also decorative or colored stones), and that the intellectual liveliness accompanying the cultural interchange of travellers then created the environment in which agriculture originated.

The pattern of human settlement from prehistoric times to our contemporary world has been determined in large measure by the availability of materials and the technological ability to work them.

Man could survive successive ice ages in the Northern Hemisphere without migrating or developing a shaggy coat like the mammoth because he had found some means of keeping himself warm — with protective covering from the skins of animals which, with his wooden and stone weapons, he could now hunt with some degree of success, but also, perhaps principally, by the control of fire, which became one of his biggest steps in controlling his environment. By the beginning of Palaeolithic (early Stone Age) times — between 800 000 and 100 000 years ago — man could produce fire at will by striking lumps of flint and iron pyrites against each other to produce sparks with which tinder, straw, or other flammable materials could be ignited.

Man's control and use of fire had immense social and cultural consequences. With fire he could not only warm his body but could also cook his food, greatly increasing the range of food resources and the ease of its preservation. Claude Levi-Strauss, the French anthropologist famous for his "structuralist" approach to culture, claims that the borderline between "nature" and "culture" lies in eating one's meat raw or eating it cooked [11]. By their role in producing and fueling fires, materials thus played a significant part in the transition from "animal-ness" to "human-ness", but more than that, fire provided a means for modifying and greatly extending the range of properties available in materials themselves.

The burning of lime for making plaster for the decoration of walls and floors seems to have been the first large-scale pyrotechnical operation [12]. It was, however, preceded by the heat treatment of flint to improve its flaking characteristics [13]. It tells something about the nature of man and of discovery that the earliest of all recorded uses of fire to modify inorganic material was in the preparation of varicolored pigments by heating natural iron oxide minerals [14].

Materials in the Beginnings of Art and Technology

Every cultural conquest, such as the use of fire, requires other cultural developments to make its use effective, and it also has unanticipated consequences in totally unforeseen areas. Containers were needed for better fires and food. The invention of pots, pans and other kitchen utensils made it possible to boil, stew, bake and fry foods as well as to broil them by direct contact with the fire. The cooking itself, and the search for materials to do it in, was perhaps the beginning of materials engineering. Furthermore, though the molding and fire hardening of clay figurines and fetishes had preceded the useful pot, it was the latter that, in the 8th millennium B.C., gave rise to the development of industry. Clay was the first inorganic structural material to be given completely new properties as a result of an intentional operation upon it by human beings. Though stone, wood, hides and bone had earlier been beautifully formed into tools and utensils, their substance had remained essentially unchanged. The ability to make a hard stone from soft and moldable clay not only unfolded into useful objects, but the realization that man could change the innermost nature of natural materials must have had a profound impact upon his view of his powers; it gave him confidence to search for new materials at an ever increasing rate.

It was in the decoration of pottery that man experimented with the effects of fire upon a wide range of mineral substances. Glazing, the forerunner of glass, certainly came therefrom, and it is probable that experiments with mineral colors on pottery led to the discovery of the reduction of metals from their ores toward the end of the 5th millennium B. C. Even earlier, man's urge to art had inspired the discovery and application of many metallic minerals as pigments [15].

From late Paleolithic times come the great cave paintings representing hunting scenes in realistic detail, executed with such mastery that, when they were discovered by chance in the caves at Altamira, Spain, in 1879 and later in Lascaux, France, many found it difficult to believe that they had been done by primitive man. These paintings provide early evidence of man's awareness of the special properties of iron ore, manganese ore and other minerals. He sensed qualitative differences that depended on chemical and physical properties quite invisible to him, but on which much of modern industry was later to be based.

Long before this, man had sensitively used the properties of other materials in art. He had made sculpture in ivory, stone, rock, clay and countless more-perishable materials. Though it is often said that his ability to do this came from the increased leisure time released by the efficiency of his hunting following the development of tools and weapons, it is more likely that the exercise of his explorative tendencies, his aesthetic curiosity, was one of the factors that from the very first gave him a unique evolutionary advantage among other animals. Interaction with materials at this level was both easy and rewarding and it was probably a necessary preliminary to the selection of the more imaginative and adaptable biological mutants that were to follow. In culture as in biology, man possessed more than the rudiments of technology when he had discovered and prepared his materials for painting and had developed methods of working them with fingertip and brush, crayons and spray. He also had used specialized tools to sculpt stone and to mold clay at about the same time he learned to finish stone abrasively, and so was freed from dependence on flakeable flint since could then adapt commoner, harder, polycrystalline rocks such as basalt and granite for his tools.

As in the case of the use of fire by man, the next great innovation in another field of technology, agriculture, was accompanied by a diverse series of auxiliary changes. Man had to develop a whole new set of tools: the hoe to till the ground, the sickle to reap the grain, some kind of flail to thresh the grain, and the quern (mill) to grind it. These tools were made of stone and wood; they were not very efficient. Nevertheless, agriculture was able to provide man with a surer source of food than could be obtained through the older technology of hunting, and it required concomitant advances in materials. Not the least important were fired ceramics which provided the pots needed for cooking, as well as larger containers for rodent-proof storage of crops.

The introduction of agriculture meant that the supply of animal skins from hunting was diminished. Man had to find substitutes among vegetable fibers, things such as reeds, flax, or cotton, and to utilize the hair of the animals which he had learned to domesticate. Some of these fibers had been used before, especially in woven mats, fences, building components and basketry, but mainly for clothing. So textiles developed and textiles inspired new machines: a spinning device (the spindle with its inertia-driven whorl) and a loom for weaving the threads into cloth. The patterns he worked into textiles and painted on his pots gave him practical contact with elements of geometry and with the relationships between short-range symmetry and long-range pattern which reappear in today's structure-based science.

Because the implements and weapons of our prehistoric forebears are crude and primitive in comparison with today's materials and machines, we should not be misled into downgrading the degree of skill which Stone Age man possessed. When, a few years ago, a class at the University of California was provided with a pile of flintstones and given the task of shaping simple stone implements from them, they found that even after many hours of repeated trials, they could not produce a tool that would have sufficed even for a run-of-the-mill Stone Age man [16]. But experience breeds skill and it is a combination of tradition and invention that aided in man's progressive evolution [17].

The great Neolithic technological revolution — with its development of agriculture and fairly large-scale settled communities — occurred some tens upon tens of thousands of years after man had already mastered his implements of stone and had achieved his intellectual and physical evolution. It set into movement a whole series of technological and cultural changes within the next two millenia which thoroughly transformed man's relations with nature and with his fellow man, and, most important, his thoughts about change

and his prospects of the future. While the process might seem slow to us today, it was dynamic by the standards of the preceding ages.

Whether or not the urban society preceded or followed the agricultural revolution, it seems almost certain that the city provided conditions that accelerated man's journey along the path towards civilization; indeed, the two are almost synonymous. During the period from about 5000 to 3000 B.C., two millenia after the introduction of agriculture, a series of basic inventions appeared [18]. Man developed a high temperature kiln he learned to smelt and employ metals and to harness animals. He invented the plow, the wheeled cart, the sailing ship and writing. Communication and commerce based on specialized skills and localized raw materials both enabled and depended upon central government together with reinforcing religious, social and scientific concepts. The great empires in Mesopotamia and Egypt, the forerunners of our Western civilization, were based on the interaction of many institutions and the ideas and muscles of many men, but materials were necessary for them to become effective. Indeed, the characteristics of this early period are mainly an interplay between principles of human organization and the discovery of the properties of matter as they resided in a wide diversity of materials. Both tools and buildings were simple; mechanisms comparable in ingenuity to the materials used in the decorative arts of Sumer, Egypt and Greece do not appear until much later. All, as far as we can tell, were based on experience and empiricism with little help from theory.

CHAPTER 4. BRONZE AND IRON AGES

Stages of Civilization Based on Materials Development

Stone was eventually supplemented by copper, and copper led to alloys, most notably bronze. Near the end of the period under discussion, bronze in turn was partially displaced by iron. So important is the change in the materials base of a civilization that the materials themselves have given rise to the names of the ages — the Stone Age, the Bronze Age and the Iron Age. In the 19th century after much groundwork both literally and figuratively by geologists, paleontologists and archeologists, these terms came to supersede both the poet's gold and silver ages and the philosopher's division of the past into periods based on religious, political, or cultural characteristics [19]. Oddly, the most critical stage, and the one that has left the best record, that of ceramics, was overlooked.

There were no sharp chronological breaking points between the three ages, nor did the switch from one material to another take place everywhere at the same time. Even, for example, in those areas where bronze tools and weapons came into use, stone tools and weapons remained on the scene for a long time. Similarly, iron did not immediately replace bronze, and indeed there were still some civilizations which passed directly from stone to iron and some which, from indifference or from lack of knowledge, never adopted either metal. As a matter of fact, the first tools and weapons of iron were probably inferior to the contemporary bronze tools whose technology had been known for over two millenia. At first, the advantage of iron over bronze was based on economics, not superior quality. Iron was laborious to smelt, but it could be made from widespread common minerals. A monarch could arm his entire army with iron swords, instead of just a few soldiers with bronze swords when the rest would have to fight with sticks and bows and arrows. With iron came a quantitative factor that had profound social, economic and political consequences for all aspects of culture [20].

Native metals, like gold, silver and copper, were hammered into decorative objects during the 8th millennium B.C. in an area stretching from Anatolia to the edge of Iran's central desert, during the 5th millennium B.C. in the Lake Superior region of North America, and during the mid-2nd millennium B.C. in South America. However, it was not until man learned to smelt metals and reduce them from their ores, to melt and cast them, that metallurgy proper can be said to have begun. Again, the early advantage was only an economic one, the mineral ores of copper being vastly more abundant than is the native metal, but the way was opened for alloying and the discovery of entirely unsuspected properties. Moreover, with molten metal, casting into complicated shapes became possible.

The discovery of smelting has left no records. Given the availability of adequately high temperatures in pottery kilns and the use of metal oxides for decoration, drops of reduced metal could well have been produced repeatedly before the significance was grasped. But once it was, empirical experiments with manipulation of the fire and the selection of the appropriate heavy, colored minerals would have given the desired materials with reasonable efficiency. A kiln works best with a long-flame fuel such as wood; smelting is best done with charcoal and with a blast from a blowpipe or bellows, but the time when these were first used has yet to be established. The first alloys were those of copper and arsenic, which may have been made at first unintentionally by smelting ores containing the two elements, though there is evidence for the conscious use of the metallic mineral algodonite (approximately Cu_8As) as an intentional addition during the casting operation [21]. Whatever their origin, the alloys are superior to pure copper in castability and in hardness, without loss of the essential metallic property of malleability, and their use marks the discovery of a vastly important metallurgical principle. For a thousand years, these alloys were exploited, until finally they were largely replaced by bronze, an alloy made from a heavy, readily identifiable, though scarce, mineral, and having somewhat superior properties to those of the copper arsenic alloys; there was also the added advantage that those who knew how to make it lived longer!

A lively argument is currently going on among archeologists as to whether the original discovery of bronze took place in the region of Anatolia and the adjacent countries to the South and East or in Eastern Europe — or independently in both [22]. Whatever the evolutionary process of the development of metallurgy, there is no doubt that it had profound social, economic and political consequences.

Though the earliest stone industry and commerce had required some organized system of production, and division of labor was well advanced in connection with large irrigation and building projects [23], the use of metals fostered a higher degree of specialization and diversity of skills; it also required communication and coordination to a degree previously unknown. Both trade and transportation owe much of their development to the requirements of materials technology: not only ores, requiring bulk transportation over great distances from foreign lands, but also precious objects for the luxury trade, such as amber, gem stones, gold and silver jewelry, fine decorated ceramics and eventually glass.

The search for ways of working materials prompted man's first use of machines to guide the power of his muscles. Rotary motion had many applications that were more influential than the well-known cartwheel. Perhaps beginning with the child's spinning top, it was the basis of many devices, the most important of which were: the drill for bead-making, stone-working and seal-cutting; the thread-maker's spindle; the quern; and above all the potter's wheel [24]. These provided the foundation for the earliest mechanized industries and were steps toward the mass-production factories of the 20th century.

Materials development had an impact on culture in other ways than through the improvement of artifacts. This can perhaps best be seen in the development of writing. The growth of commerce and government stimulated the need for records. Little geometrically shaped pieces of fire-hardened clay seem to have been used as tallies to accompany goods in the 9th millennium B.C. and it has been postulated that sketches of them on the outside of protective clay envelopes became the first writing [25]. The materials to produce the records undoubtedly influenced the nature of the writing itself and, if modern linguistic scholars are correct, probably some details of the language structure and hence the mode of thought.

Marshall McLuhan has popularized the phrase, "the medium is the message". A painting, a poem, a print, a pot, a line of type, a ballet, a piece of carved sculpture, a hammered goldsmith's work, or a TV image all convey differences in sensory perceptions which form the basis of human communication [26], and we might guess that the same process occurred at the very beginning of art and purposeful records. The Sumerians in the Tigris–Euphrates valley had abundant clay to serve as their stationery, and the sharp stylus employed with it did not allow a cursive writing to develop; did this have some impact on the ways in which they thought, spoke and acted? The Egyptians, in contrast, could adapt the interwoven fibers of a reed growing in the Nile delta to produce a more flexible

medium, papyrus, on which they could write with brushes and ink in less restricted ways. Thus, the differences between the cuneiform and hieroglyphic writing were dependent on the differences in materials available, quite as much as were the mud-brick and stone architecture of their respective regions. At the time, the visual arts were probably more significant than writing, for relatively few people, except professional scribes, would have been influenced by the latter. Certainly, our retrospective view of old civilizations depends on the preservation of art in material form, and the material embodiment of thought and symbol in the visual environment must have modified the experience and behavior of ancient peoples, even as it does today.

Emergence of Iron and Steel

The replacement of copper and bronze by iron began about 1200 B.C. Iron had been produced long before then because iron ores are prevalent and easily reduced at temperatures comparable to those required for smelting copper. However, the iron was probably not recognized as such, because at those temperatures it is not melted but remains as a loose sponge of particles surrounded by slag and ash, being easily crumbled or pulverized and having no obvious metallic properties. If, on the other hand, the porous mass is hammered vigorously while hot, the particles weld together, the slag is forced out and bars of wrought iron are produced.

Though metallic iron may have been previously seen as occasional lumpy by-products from lead and copper smelting (in which iron oxides were used to make siliceous impurities in the iron more fusible), its intentional smelting is commonly attributed to the Hittites, an Anatolian people, in about 1500 B.C. The Hittite monopoly of ferrous knowledge was dispersed with the empire in about 1200 B.C., but it took almost another 500 years before iron came into general use and displaced the mature metallurgy of bronze. Each ore had its own problems with metalloid and rocky impurities [27]. Immense skill was needed to remove the oxygen in the ore by reaction with the charcoal fuel without allowing subsequent absorption of carbon to a point where the reduced metal became brittle.

Certain forms of iron — those to which the name steel was once limited — can become intensely hard when heated red hot and quenched in water. This truly marvelous transmutation of properties must have been observed quite early, but its significance would have been hard to grasp and, in any case, it could not be put to use until some means of controlling the carbon content had been developed. Since the presence of carbon as the essential prerequisite was not known until the end of the 18th century A.D., good results were achieved only by a slowly learned empirical rule-of-thumb schedule of the entire furnace regimen. Even the process of partial softening, today called tempering, was very late in appearing (perhaps in the 16th century) and early "tempering" was actually hardening done in a single quenching operation, in which the steel was withdrawn from the cooling bath at precisely the right moment. It is not surprising that this was rarely successful. Carburized and quenched tools began to appear in 8th century B.C. sites, and it has been suggested [28] that the vast increase in the use of iron at that time was a result of the discovery of methods of controlling the carburization and heat-treatment processes. However, the majority of objects, then as now, were of low carbon content and not hardened or even hardenable. Yet, even without hardening, iron had no difficulty in supplanting bronze for many applications. Its abundance meant that the elite could not control it. Iron was the "democratic" metal because a rise in the living standards among larger masses of population was obtainable through its application in tools and implements [29].

The wide distribution of iron over the earth's surface enabled it to serve for tools and agricultural implements as well as weapons of war and precious objects for the ruling households. Before 1000 B.C., there are records of iron hoes, plowshares, sickles and knives in use in Palestine. From about 700 B.C., iron axes came into play for clearing forest land in Europe and for agricultural purposes. Iron tools together with evolving organization arrangements greatly increased the productivity of agriculture, giving a surplus which could support large numbers of specialized craftsmen whose products, in turn, could become generally available instead of being monopolized by the wealthiest ruling circles. Furthermore, tools formerly made of bronze or stone — such as adzes, axes, chisels, drills,

hammers, gravers, saws, gauges — could be made less expensively and more satisfactorily in iron. The new tools allowed for new methods of working materials: forging in dies, the stamping and punching of coins, and, many years later, developments such as the drawing of wire and the rolling of sheet and rod. These metalworking methods were easily harnessed to water power when it appeared and opened up ways of making more serviceable and cheaper products. Though it was not immediately exploited, the strength of metals permitted the construction of delicate machines. Iron was at first used structurally only for reinforcing joints in stone or wood, but later its strength and stability were combined with precision in creating the modern machine tool, and its large-scale fabrication also made modern architecture possible.

CHAPTER 5. MATERIALS IN CLASSICAL CIVILIZATION

Development of Hydraulic Cement by the Romans — A Materials Innovation

It has been claimed that bronze made for the centralization of economic power as well as the concentration of political authority in the hands of an aristocratic few, while iron broadened the economic strength to a larger class of traders and craftsmen and so led to the decentralization of power and eventually to the formation of Athenian democracy.

Although the classical civilization of Greece rather fully exploited the possibilities offered by metals and other materials available to them from preceding ages, producing beautifully wrought ceramics, exquisite jewelry, superb sculpture, and an architecture which still represents one of the peaks of the Western cultural and aesthetic tradition, they did little to innovate in the field of materials themselves.

The same is true of the Romans who acquired a great reputation as engineers, and rightly so, but this rests largely upon the monumental scale of their engineering endeavors — the great roads, aqueducts and public structures — rather than upon any great mechanical innovations or the discovery of new materials.

There is one exception to this generalization. The Romans did introduce a new building material: hydraulic concrete. The use of lime mortar is extremely old, probably even preceding the firing of pottery, and lime plaster was used for floor and wall covering, for minor works of art and later for the lining of water reservoirs and channels. It can be made by firing limestone at a moderate red heat; it sets hard when mixed with water and allowed slowly to react with carbon dioxide in the air. If, however, the limestone contains alumina and silica (geologically from clay) and is fired at a higher temperature, a material of the class later to be called hydraulic, or Portland, cement is formed. After grinding and mixing with water, this sets by the crystallization of hydrated silicates, even when air is excluded, and develops high strength. Similar cements based on the reactive formation of silicate crystals in an aqueous medium enabled many of the great 19th century achievements in civil engineering and they still provide the most ubiquitous artificial material in use today. The Romans were fortunate in having available large quantities of volcanic ash, pozzuolana, which, when mixed with lime, gave such a cement. They exploited it to extremely good purpose (reinforced with stone rubble or with hard bricks) in the construction of buildings, bridges and aqueducts. Massive foundations and columns were much more easily built than with the older fitted-stone construction, and unlike mortar, the cement was waterproof. By combining the new cement with the structural device of the arch, the Romans could roof-over large areas without the obstructions of columns [30].

The Primary Role of Empiricism in Materials Advances

The case of hydraulic cement is representative of materials usage from antiquity until modern times. Namely, it was developed entirely on an empirical basis, without much in the way of any science to explain the useful properties. Most types of material in use today were discovered centuries before there was any science to aid them; in fact, the science arose from the discoveries of practice rather than the other way round. The great Greek philosophers, to be sure, had worried about the nature of matter and the three states in which it exists -- solid, liquid and gas.

These, indeed, constitute three of the four famous elements of Aristotle which dominated philosophy for nearly 2000 years. His earth, water and air represent fine physical insight, but they had to be rejected by chemists in their search for compositional elements [31]. But, in any case, it was not philosophy that guided advance. The main contribution to early understanding came from the more intelligent empirical workers who discovered new materials, new reactions and new types of behavior among the grand diversity of substances whose properties could be reproduced but not explained except on an *ad hoc* basis. Through most of history, it has been the almost sensual experience with that complex aggregation of properties summed up in the term the "nature" of the material that has guided empirical search for new materials and modifications of old ones. The ability to go beyond such empiricism and to plan tests on the basis of an adequate theory of the composition–structure–property relationships is a 20th century phenomenon and had to await a quite late stage in the development of science. The science needed was a kind that was slow to emerge because of the extreme complexity of the problems involved.

Unlike astronomy, there was little place for accurate measurements of geometry in materials and those who sought to find rules were perpetually frustrated. The curious experimenter, however, by mixing, heating and working materials in a myriad of ways did uncover virtually all of the materials with properties that were significant to him, namely, strength, malleability, corrosion resistance, color, texture and fusibility. Science began to be helpful much later when chemical analysis — an outgrowth of the metallurgists' methods of testing the fineness of precious metal objects or bullion, or the metal content in ores of all kinds before going to full-scale operation — advanced to the point where it showed that there were only a limited number of chemical elements and that ostensibly similar materials, differing in their nature, contained different impurities. Then it was discovered that chemical substances of identical composition could differ in their internal structure, and finally structure became relatable to properties in a definite way; only then was it possible to modify the structure purposefully to achieve a desired effect [32].

Some Proposed Connections Between Materials and Roman History

There have been many interpretations of the decline and fall of the Great Roman Empire. The early Christian apologists claimed that Rome fell because it was wicked and immoral; in the 18th century, Gibbon blamed the fall of Rome upon Christianity itself. Since that time, the "fall" has been attributed to numerous factors: political, economic, military, cultural and the like. It is not surprising, with the recent interest in the history of technology, that technological interpretations of Rome's decline have begun to appear, and some of these center on Rome's use of materials. A few years ago, Gilfillan [33] claimed that the decline of Rome was due to a decline in the birth rate of the Roman patrician class as a result of dysgenic lead poisoning. Although all Romans got a goodly intake from their lead-lined water system, the elite drank more than its share of wine from lead vessels and this was thought to reduce the fertility of the leaders! Lately [34], a geochemist has claimed that Rome's troubles derived from the economic effects of the enforced decline in silver production which began about 200 A.D. because the mines had become so deep that they could no longer be cleared of water with the technical means available.

CHAPTER 6. MEDIEVAL MATERIALS

Materials Processing and Machine Power

Throughout the first millennium after Christ, about the only places where ancient techniques of making and working materials underwent improvement were outside Europe — in the Arab World, Iran, India and the Far East. Textiles, ceramics, articles in silver and bronze and iron of excellent quality appeared. That portentous new material, paper, originated in China and began its Western diffusion. Though the armorers of the Western world were steadily improving their products, the Crusaders of the 12th century had no steel which could match that of the Saracen sword. (The Japanese sword surpassed the Islamic one by an even greater margin than the latter did the European.) However, not for several centuries did these Oriental superiorities in materials processing have any effect upon the materials science or technology of contemporary Western Christendom.

For all this, the first significant literature on materials is European — the *Treatise on Divers Arts* written about 1123, by a Benedictine monk under the pseudonym Theophilus [35]. He was a practical metalworker and he described in full practical detail all the arts necessary for the embellishment of the church, such as the making of chalices, stained-glass windows, bells, organs, painted panels and illuminated manuscripts.

Theophilus was no materials engineer in the modern sense, but he was a craftsman, probably the historical goldsmith Roger of Helmarshausen, some of whose work has survived. His knowledge of matter was the directly sensed, intuitive understanding that comes from constantly handling a wide variety of substances under different conditions. His *Treatise* is essentially a factual "how to" book, containing many exhortations to watch carefully for subtle changes in the materials being processed but with no trace of theoretical explanation. Theory does not appear in treatises intended to help the practical worker in materials until 600 years later — well into the 18th century.

Although the nature of materials themselves did not change greatly in Western Europe during the Middle Ages, a number of mechanical inventions facilitated both their production and their shaping [36]. The first widespread application of power in processing materials was in grinding grain. This practice considerably increased when windpower supplemented the older waterpower, with the technique, as so much else, diffusing from the East. Textiles at first benefited only by the use of waterpower in the fulling process, but the mechanically simpler and more laborious metallurgical processes changed substantially. In ironworking, waterpower was applied successively to bellows, to hammers and eventually (15th century) to slitting, rolling and wire drawing.

A series of mechanical innovations and improvements also led to advances in the manufacturing and processing of other materials. Plant ash to make glass was replaced by more-or-less pure soda, and the furnaces to melt it in became larger. Textile looms improved, especially with the introduction (from China) of the draw loom. Even more important was the development, near the close of the 13th century, of the spinning wheel in place of the ancient handspun whorl, virtually unchanged since prehistoric times.

Power not only enabled the scale of operation to be increased in iron-working, but the product was more uniform because of the extensive working that was possible. In addition, the use of power changed the basic chemistry of the process. Although a large furnace is not needed in order to produce molten cast iron, it is much more easily made in a tall shaft furnace driven by powerful bellows than in a low hearth. Cast iron first appeared in Europe in the 14th century, following a sequence of developments which is unclear but which certainly involved power-driven bellows, larger furnaces, and perhaps hints from the East. To begin with, cast iron was used only as an intermediate stage in the making of steel or wrought iron, and it was developed for its efficiency in separating iron from the ore by production of both metal and slag in liquid form. However, cast iron that contains enough carbon to be fusible is brittle, and it took Europeans some time to realize its utility, although it had long been used in the Far East.

Ferrous Metallurgy

By the beginning of the 15th century, cast iron containing about 3% carbon and commonly about 1% silicon and which melts at a temperature of about 1200 °C in comparison with 1540 °C for pure iron had found three distinct uses: as a bath in which to immerse wrought iron in order to convert it into steel; as a material to be cast in molds to produce objects like pots, fire irons and fireback more cheaply; and, most important of all, as the raw material for the next stage of iron manufacture.

The age-old process of directly smelting the ore with charcoal and flux in an open hearth or low shaft furnace yielded a product of low-carbon material in the form of an unmelted spongy mass, which was forged to expel slag, to consolidate it and shape it. It was inefficient because of the large amount of iron that remained in the slag, and the iron was defective because of the slag remaining in it. The wrought iron produced from cast iron by the new finery process was made by oxidizing the carbon and silicon in cast iron instead of by the direct reduction of the iron oxide ore. The

two-stage indirect process gradually displaced the direct method in all technologically advanced countries. Its main justification was economic efficiency, for the resulting product was still wrought iron or steel, finished below its melting point and containing many internal inclusions of iron silicate slag. In the late 18th century, the small hearth was replaced by a reverberatory puddling furnace which gave much larger output, but neither the chemistry nor the product was significantly different from that of the early finery [37].

It was only with the possibility of obtaining temperatures high enough to melt low-carbon iron — essentially the time of Bessemer and Siemens in the 1860's — that slag-free ductile iron became commercially possible. The very meaning of the word "steel" was changed in the process, for the word, previously restricted to quench-hardenable medium- and high-carbon steel for tools, was appropriated by salesmen of the new product because of its implication of superiority.

Contributions of Empiricism and Theory

Earlier developments in iron and steel metallurgy had occurred with no assistance from theory, which, such as it was, was far behind practice. The Aristotelean theory of matter, essentially unchallenged in medieval times, recognized the solid, liquid and gaseous states of matter in three of the four elements — earth, water, air and fire. The theory encompassed the various properties of materials but was wrong in attributing their origin to the combination of qualities rather than things. Medieval alchemists in their search for a relation between the qualities of matter and the principles of the universe elaborated this theory considerably. One of their goals — transmutation — was to change the association of qualities in natural bodies. In the days before the chemical elements had been identified, this was a perfectly sensible aim. What more proof of the validity of transmutation does one need than the change in quality of steel reproducibly accomplished by fire and water? Or the transmutation of ash and sand into a brilliant glass gem, and mud into a glorious Attic vase or Sung celadon pot? Or the conversion of copper into golden brass? Of course, today we know that it is impossible to duplicate simultaneously all the properties of gold in the absence of atomic nuclei having a positive charge 79. One way to secure a desired property is still to select the chemical entities involved but much can also be done by changing the structure of substances. Such modern alchemy is more solid-state physics than it is chemistry, but it could not have appeared until after chemists had unraveled the nature and number of the elements.

Urged on by the manifestly great changes of properties accompanying chemical operations, the alchemists worked on the same things that concerned the practical metallurgist, potter and dyer of their day, but the two groups interacted not at all. In retrospect one can see that the alchemist's concern with properties was not far from the motivation of the present-day materials scientist and engineer. They were right in believing that the property changes accompanying transmutation were manifestations of the primary principles of the universe, but they missed the significance of the underlying structure. Moreover, they overvalued a theory that was too ambitious and so their literature is now of more value to students of psychology, mysticism and art than it is as a direct forerunner of modern materials science. Yet the alchemists — especially the Arabic practitioners of the art — discovered some important substances; they developed chemical apparatus and processes which are basic to science today and they represent an important tradition in theoretically motivated laboratory operations, even if they failed to correct their theory by the results of well-planned critical experiments [38]. This approach proved sterile during the Middle Ages, while the workshop tradition represented by Theophilus led to many advances. The collaboration between the two approaches, which is the very basis and principal characteristic of today's emerging MSE, simply did not occur.

Impacts of Printing and Gunpowder

Two major technological developments helped precipitate the changes that signalized the close of the Middle Ages and the beginning of modern times: printing and gunpowder. Both of these had earlier roots in Chinese technology and both were intimately related to materials.

In the case of printing [39], all the necessary separate elements were in general use in Western Europe by the middle of the 15th century: paper, presses, ink and, if not moveable type, at least wood-block printing of designs on textiles and pictures and text on paper, and separate punches to impress letters and words on coins and other metalwork. But they had not been put together in Europe. Papyrus and parchment had been known in ancient times. Paper made of vegetable fiber had been invented in China a thousand years earlier and had been introduced into Spain by the Arabs during the 12th century. Simple presses were already in use for making wine and oil, while linseed-oil-based ink (another essential element in the printing process) had been developed by artists a short time previously.

The idea for the most important element needed for mass production of verbal communication — reusable individual type — probably came to Europe from the Orient, although the history is obscure. By the 11th century, Chinese printers were working with baked ceramic type mounted on a backing plate with an adhesive and removable for reuse. By the 14th century in Korea, even cast bronze type was known.

Shortly after 1440 in Europe, everything came together in an environment so receptive that the development was almost explosive. Though there may have been experiments in the Lowlands, the successful combination of all the factors occurred in Mainz in Germany, where Johann Gutenberg began experiments in the casting of metal type during the 1440's. By 1445 he and his associates were able to produce a magnificent book, the *Gutenberg Bible*, still one of the finest examples of European printing. It consists of 643 leaves, about 40 cm × 29 cm in size, printed on both sides with gothic type in two columns. Some chapter headings were printed in red, others inserted by hand. Part of the edition was printed on paper, part on vellum, the traditional material for permanence or prestige. Unlike the earlier Oriental type, Gutenberg's was cast in a metal mold having a replaceable matrix with a stamped impression of the letter, arranged so that the body of the type was exactly rectangular and would lock firmly together line-by-line within the form for each page. Both the metal and the mold were adapted from earlier pewterer's practice. Thus, a new technique for mass production and communication was established, ushering in a potential instrument for mass education. Modern times were beginning.

The political and economic environment had been strongly influenced somewhat earlier by the introduction of gunpowder in Western Europe. Explosive mixtures for holiday firecrackers had been used for centuries in China; it was only in the "civilized" West that gunpowder was first employed to enable man to kill his fellowman. Here too, it is uncertain whether the introduction of gunpowder in the West was a result of independent discovery or diffusion from the Far East. At any rate, the application and development was different and prompt. As early as 1325, primitive cannon were built in the West for throwing darts, arrows and heavy stone balls, in competition with the mechanical artillery (the ballista) familiar since the days of the Romans, which were displaced completely by the middle of the 16th century. By 1450, the musket had appeared and began to render the cross-bow and long-bow obsolete.

By 1500, bombards, mortars and explosive mines caused the medieval elements of warfare — the fortified castle and the individual armored knight — to lose their military importance and contributed to the decline of the feudal nobility [40]. (Another technical device, the stirrup, had aided their rise [41].) Accordingly, the changes in the technology of warfare aided in the process of administrative and territorial consolidation which was to give birth to the national state and transform the map of Europe.

Even the layout of cities changed as a result of the new methods of warfare: the round towers and high straight walls no longer afforded good defense in the age of cannon; they were replaced by geometrically planned walls and arranged so that every face could be enfiladed.

Military needs sparked a great development in the scale of the material-producing industries during the Renaissance, but agriculture, construction and the generally rising standard of living also contributed and benefited. The new supply of silver coming from Spanish operations in the New World and, no less, from the development of the liquation process for recovering silver from German copper upset the monetary balance of Europe. Silver, pewter, brass, wood and the greatly increased production of glazed ceramic vied with each other for domestic attention, and glass democratically appeared in more windows and on more tables.

16th Century Publications on Materials

We know much more about material-producing processes in the 16th century than we do of earlier ages, because the printing press gave a wider audience and made it worthwhile for men to write down the details of their craft in order to instruct others rather than to keep their trade secrets. Some of our most famous treatises on materials technology date from the 16th century and the best of these continued to be reprinted over 150 years later — an indication that practices were not advancing rapidly.

The most famous of these treatises is the *de Re Metallica* [42] by Georg Bauer (Latin, Georgius Agricola) published posthumously in 1556. Agricola was a highly literate and intellectually curious physician living in Bohemian Joachimstal and Silesian Chemnitz, both mining and smelting towns, and his systematic factual descriptions of minerals, mining and smelting operations, all excellently illustrated, shed much light on the devices and techniques of the times. Agricola writes of large-scale industrial operations, with a center of interest far removed from the craftsman's workshop by Theophilus centuries earlier. The scale is that of a capitalistic enterprise. Nevertheless, Agricola still thought in the same terms as did Theophilus; his *de Re Metallica* is simply a description of actual practice, devoid of any theoretical principles, though in other works, most notably his *de Natura Fossilium* (1546), he did speculate fruitfully on the nature and origin of minerals.

Sixteen years earlier, the Italian foundryman Vannocio Biringuccio had published his *de la Pirotechnia*, which is much broader in scope [43]. It has less detail on the smelting operations, but is excellent on all aspects of casting and working metals and has good discussions of glassmaking, smithy operations, the casting of bells and sculpture, and the manufacture of cannon and gunpowder. He says that the bronze founder looks like a chimney sweep, is in perpetual danger of a fatal accident and fearful of the outcome of each casting, and is regarded as a fool by his countrymen, "but with all this it is a profitable and skilled art and in large part delightful". Biringuccio says that fortune will favor you if you take proper precautions in doing your work in the foundry and he advocates the empirical approach, almost as a modern experimentalist might, in these words, "It is necessary to find the true method by doing it again and again, always varying the procedure and then stopping at the best". His section on casting, boring and mounting of cannon is specially good and shows how dependent all this was on the earlier technique of the bell founder, which he also meticulously reports.

Both Agricola and Biringuccio describe the quantitative analytical methods then in use for assaying ores and metallurgical products. Even better on this aspect of chemistry is the great treatise of Lazarus Ercker, the *Beschreibung allerfürnemisten mineralischen Ertzt und Bergwercksarten*, published in Prague in 1574 [44]. Ercker's exposition of the assayer's art displays intimate knowledge of the reactions, miscibilities and seperations of the common metals and oxides, sulfides, slags and fluxes as well as sophisticated methods of cupelling, parting with acid etc., and is thoroughly quantitative in outlook and intent.

In all these early writings, there is a bias toward the precious metals, gold and silver. Even Biringuccio, who was concerned with end-use far more than other writers, had very little to say about iron despite the fact that this was the most common metal then, as now. The rough labor of the smith was almost beneath the notice of educated men. There is no comprehensive book devoted to iron until that of R.A.F. de Réaumur published in 1722 [45]. This was preceded only by occasional references in literary works and by an anonymous little treatise on the hardening and etching of iron (1532), a Polish poem of 1612 (*Officina Ferraria* by W. Rozdienski) [46] and a fine description of locksmiths' and skilled ironworkers' operations by Mathurin Jousse in 1627 [47]. Though glass is treated in fair detail by Biringuccio, the first book devoted entirely to it is that by Neri in 1612.

Other practical arts gradually received a place in the visible literature. Piccolpasso's unpublished manuscript of 1550 has fine detail on all stages of ceramic manufacture, glazing and decoration [48]. The *Plictho* of Gioanventura Rosetti (1548) has descriptions on dyeing [49]. Other booklets give innumerable recipes for the making of ink, soldering, gilding, removing spots, along with many cosmetic and household craft recipes [50]. The sudden appearance of this literature in print does not mean that the processes described were new in the 16th century; indeed, most of them had been going around for centuries, circulated by word-of-mouth or in rough manuscripts of a form and content that no respectable librarian would deem worth keeping.

If in this treatment we seem to have over-emphasized the 16th century, it is because intimate records become available for the first time of techniques built upon many centuries of slow consolidation of changes. These writings show vividly how much can be done without the benefit of science, but at their own times they served to disseminate to a large and new audience knowledge of the way materials behaved; such knowledge was an essential basis for later scientific attack.

Agricola wrote in Latin, but otherwise all of this literature was in the vernacular: Italian, French or German. It was part of the Reformation. Instead of theoretical dogma handed down from on high for intellectual gratification, it was down-to-earth practical information for the workshop and kitchen. The realization that theory could help this kind of practice was quite slow in emerging and a real science of materials had to wait for another three centuries. In the meantime, the separate components of ferrous and nonferrous metallurgy, ceramics, dyeing, fiber technology, organic polymers and structural engineering pursued their own separate lines of development, and the basic sciences of chemistry and physics slowly generated an understanding that would help explain practice, enrich and extend it. Together, this all served to provide the facts and viewpoints that would eventually knit into the new grouping of man's knowledge and activity known as materials science and engineering.

CHAPTER 7. THE START OF A SCIENTIFIC MATERIALS TECHNOLOGY BASED ON CHEMISTRY

Toward the Interplay of Science and Practice in Materials Technology

The linking of theoretical understanding with practical applications, the hallmark of MSE, did not occur with the Scientific Revolution of the 17th century nor with the Industrial Revolution of the 18th and 19th centuries. Although tremendous advances occurred during the 17th to 19th centuries in scientific understanding of the nature and operation of the physical universe at both atomic and cosmic levels, very little of this could find direct connection to the materials made and used by man. True, major transformations were taking place in the processing and application of old materials, and new ones were being developed, but these were largely the product of empirical advances within materials technology itself, owing little to contemporary scientific understanding.

Indeed, the very complications of the useful properties of materials precluded their understanding by the necessarily simplistic methods of rigorous science. Though kinetics and elasticity were simple enough to be handled by the new mathematics, the mechanics of plasticity and fracture were utterly beyond it. Unsuspected variations in composition and structure produced changes in properties that could be manipulated only by those who enjoyed messy reality. Science could advance only by ignoring these problems and concentrating instead on other fields in which it was possible, both theoretically and experimentally, to exclude unknown, unwanted, or uncontrollable variables — in brief, science advanced by the process of reductionism, reducing the problem to manageable parts.

Eventually, of course, on the fragmentary knowledge so acquired, it became possible to deal with real materials, but those properties that are structure sensitive — which includes most of the interesting properties of matter from the user's viewpoint — have been very late in succumbing. It would surely have delayed understanding had some superpower insisted that physicists work upon important but unsolvable (at that time) properties of matter. Materials practitioners cannot disregard those aspects of the behavior of matter simply because a scientist cannot deal with them. The development of the different threads of knowledge proceeds each at its own pace. Eventually, however, they all go in a higher synthesis. However, the history of MSE shows that this synthesis is far more than the putting together of exact understanding of many parts; it is putting this understanding into a higher, or at least broader, framework combining experience as well as logic. All levels, all viewpoints must interact and the present tension between the different parts of the materials profession gives ground for hope that new methods of managing this difficult synthesis are beginning to emerge. It is rare for both attitudes of mind to be combined in one individual, but a tolerance, indeed an enjoyment, of opposing points-of-view is one of the things that makes MSE so interesting today.

In the past, even when scientific advances occurred which might have illumined the nature and structure of materials, their significance was not immediately apparent to the practitioner and the impact on technology was delayed. With only a few exceptions, the coupling of science to engineering had to await the slow development of new concepts, a tolerance for new approaches, and the establishment of new institutions to create a hybrid form, engineering science, or, if one prefers, scientific technology — which is basically different from both the older handbook-using technology and rigorous exclusive science [51]. This is mainly a 20th century, even a mid-20th century, development.

With hindsight, we can see how scientific advances of earlier times could have been adopted by contemporary engineers more promptly than they actually were. Nevertheless, a practical metallurgist or potter quite rightly disregarded the theoretical chemistry of 1600 A.D. as well as the physicist's ideas on matter in 1900 A.D. Both would have been quite useless to him. Yet, with the passing of time, these inapplicable approaches developed to the point where many new advances stemmed from them. We can equally wonder why scientists were frequently so obtuse as to make no attempt to investigate or to comprehend the fascinating complex problems which arose in practice. Such an approach would have been completely a-historical. It would ignore the fact that the implications of new viewpoints tend not to be apparent to men whose practice and whose ideas are in productive harmony at the time; it would also ignore the fact that science and technology had developed out of different traditions — the philosophic and scholarly on one hand, the art and craft and oral tradition on the other. A major reshuffling of attitudes and institutional devices was essential before the two could be brought together in a fruitful relationship; what is more, science and technology had to advance, each in its own way, to the point where they addressed themselves to common problems.

It was only when both science and technology had each reached a high level of development that continued progress in either depended upon concomitant advances in the other. It was then recognized that their unified actions were mutually beneficial and of service to mankind.

The Disparate Roles of Science and Practice During the 18th and 19th Centuries

If we outline briefly the developments in materials science and in materials engineering during the 18th and 19th centuries, we can see some hints of the eventual emergence of the new and fruitful relationship to which we have given the name of "scientific technology".

The story of sal ammoniac in the 18th century is instructive in this regard. Robert T. Multhauf has shown how virtually all of the chemical data needed in the various processes for producing sal ammoniac can be found in the scientific literature prior to the effective foundation of European industry. But it is difficult to prove how, if at all, the scientific knowledge was actually transmitted to the manufacturer who had to design large-scale, safe and economical equipment, conceive of interdependent processes using the by-products and build the factories producing not just one but many marketable chemicals. As Multhauf states, "it seems very probable that the obscure men who were primarily responsible for the success of that industry were beneficiaries of the literature of popular science which flourished in the mid-18th century. But if the technology of sal ammoniac was ultimately dependent upon science, the scientists played a very minor role in the industrialization of sal ammoniac production, which was accomplished primarily by men whose principal qualifications seemed to have been ingenuity and a spirit of enterprise" [52].

The great technological feats of the mid-18th century — the hallmark inventions of the Industrial Revolution — came from men without formal training in science. The mechanicians who produced them, such as James Watt, were not unlettered men and were not ignorant of the empirical science which they needed for their technical work, but this was not paced by new research at the scientific frontier [53]. James Watt did have contact with Dr. Joseph Black, the discoverer of latent and specific heat, but if Watt should share credit with anybody, it would be Matthew Boulton, the entrepreneur, rather than Joseph Black, the scientist.

This does not mean that there was no interplay between science and technology during this early period, nor that such contacts were not fruitful. Indeed, we have some very notable exceptions which prove the rule. For example, the need for bleaching and dyeing textiles and for porcelain to complete with the superb imports from the Far East stimulated basic investigations in high temperature and analytical chemistry; a virtually direct line can be traced from these technical needs to the discovery of oxygen and the analytical definition of a chemical element which was to be the basis of the Chemical Revolution of the late 18th century. The classic examples for close relationship between science and technology in the 19th century were thermodynamics and electricity. In the former case, technology presented problems for science; in the latter, science presented potentialities for technology. But beyond these simple connections, what were the customary relationships between science and technology, the interactions as well as the reactions?

Men like Carnot and Edouard Seguin, who were responsible for primary theoretical advances in the field of thermodynamics, were engineers by profession. In his investigation of energy, James Prescott Joule always started with some specific technical problem, for example the practical performance of an electrical motor with its production of work and heat. There is no doubt that the engine — the steam engine and later the internal-combustion engine and the electric motor — presented problems which attracted the attention of scientists and led to theoretical developments. But, and this is perhaps the crucial point, although technological advances spurred advances in theory, the theoretical knowledge obtained with such stimuli was slow to feed back to technology.

Lynwood Bryant has shown, as a case in point, that the important steps in the development of the heat engine came from practical men not very close to theory, and the academicians, who understood the theory, did not invent the engine. Despite this, the change from the common-sense criteria of fuel economy to a new criterion of thermal efficiency marked a step toward the domain of abstractions, of invisible things like heat and energy, and was a major development in bringing scientific technology into being [54].

The discovery of voltaic electricity as a result of the work by Galvani and Volta in 1791 to 1800 initiated a totally new period in the relationship between science and technology. Discovered in the laboratory, electricity inspired a number of empirical experimenters and gadgeteers but it found no practical use for nearly forty years, when the electric telegraph and electroplating appeared almost simultaneously. These applications provided an opportunity for many people of different intellectual and practical approaches to acquire experience with the new force [55]. The beginning of the electrical power industry lies in the design of generators for the electroplater, and widespread knowledge of circuitry came from the electric telegraph.

From our viewpoint, it should be noted that electrical science and industry both required the measurement of new properties of matter. Up to this point, virtually all interest in the properties of materials was related to their mechanical properties, color and resistance to corrosion; now attention had to be paid to electrical properties. Conductors and insulators were, of course, well known and classified. The relationship between thermal and electrical conductivity had been identified, and some studies of the magnetic properties of the simple materials had been carried out well before 1800, but the richness of the field appeared only when experiments done in connection with the first Atlantic cable showed the great differences in the conductivity of copper from different sources and eventually related conductivity to the nature of the alloy. With the transformer came studies of iron alloys in the search for lower hysteresis losses, and the science and practice never parted company thereafter.

Even in the electrical areas, however, improvements and applications continued to come from the technology more than from the science. Edison, the greatest electrical inventor of the century, was not schooled in electrical science and sometimes did things opposed to the electrical theory of the time. In Kelvin, we see a man of the future, but even he did not let his theory restrain his em-

pirical genius. Well into the 20th century, men in close practical contact with the properties of materials had a better intuitive grasp of the behavior of matter than did well-established scientists.

The mutually reinforcing attitudes of mind which eventually led men to associate in MSE at first led technologists and scientists to place emphasis on different facets of the same totality of knowledge and experience. Scientists, in the simplifications that are essential to them, must often leave out some aspect which the technologist cannot ignore and they usually overemphasize those aspects of nature that are newly discovered. It is commonplace to ridicule outmoded theories after new viewpoints have gained strength. Yet, it can be claimed that the relegation of phlogiston to the dustbin of history by the 18th century chemists was something of a loss, for the properties of metals are indeed due to a nearly intangible metallizing principle — the valence electron in the conduction band in today's quantum theory of the metallic stage. Similarly, the success of Dalton's atomic theory drew attention away from compounds that did not have simple combining proportions, and it left the very exciting properties of non-stoichiometric compounds to be rediscovered in the middle of the 20th century. Lavoisier's enthusiasm for the newly discovered oxygen not only led him to believe it to be the basis of all acids — hence its name — but also to claim that its presence was responsible for the properties of white cast iron. Both were errors which took some years to eradicate.

Contributions of Chemistry to Materials Technology

Chemistry at the end of the 18th century had turned away from the old concern with qualities and adopted a purely compositional and analytical approach to materials. This was an approach with which something clearly worthwhile could be done, whereas properties (being structure sensitive as we now know) could only be handled individually by purely *ad hoc* suppositions regarding the parts or corpuscules, which the ill-fated Cartesian viewpoint had made briefly popular. From analytical chemistry came a major triumph: new quantitative concepts of elements and atoms and molecules. These remain an essential basis of MSE although the control of composition is now seen less as an end in itself than as an easy or cheap way of obtaining a desired structure.

The discovery of the presence of carbon and its chemical role in steel was a great achievement of 18th century analytical chemistry. Indeed, until that time ignorance regarding chemical composition meant that there could be little basic conception of the nature of steel, and hence there was much confusion regarding both its definition and its production. A full understanding of the changes in the properties of steel on hardening could not be reached until it was learned in 1774 - 1781 that the carbon which helped produce the fire also entered into the makeup of the steel itself [56].

The obvious value of this and related chemical knowledge eventually brought chemists as analysts into every large industrial establishment, but it also led to a temporary disregard of some promising earlier work on structure, which had begun by observations on the fracture appearance of bellmetal, steel and other materials. The fracture test is extremely old and artisans to this day often judge the quality of their materials from the characteristic texture and color of broken surfaces. Early in the 18th century, the versatile scientist de Réamur applied quite sound structural concepts to the making and hardening of steel and malleable cast iron, as well as to porcelain. He had interests ranging all the way from advanced science to traditional practice, and he carried out much of his work specifically for the purpose of reducing the cost of materials so that the common man could enjoy beautiful objects. Réamur was the very model of a modern material scientist and engineer [57]. He had virtually no followers, for the leading physicists became increasingly absorbed by mathematical science under the influence of Newton and they joined the chemists who were proud of having thrown over the ancient intangible "qualities" for the new analytical approach.

The only scientific interest in the structure of matter at the end of the 18th century existed in the field of crystallography applied to the identification and classification of minerals. Some superb mathematics was developed around the concept of building crystals of differing shapes by stacking polyhedral units, but it failed to connect in any effective

way with atomic theory and few people even suspected that most real materials were composed of hosts of tiny imperfect crystals.

As a result, Réamur's approach, which would have been fertile in the thought and practice of metallurgy had it been followed up, lay fallow for over a century -- until Henry Clifton Sorby applied the microscope to steel (1863) and discovered that the grains which could be seen on a fractured surface were actually crystalline in nature and changed in response to composition and heat treatment. But even then, it was to take another two decades before the full significance of Sorby's discovery was recognized, when other metallurgists and engineers began to focus their attention on structure as well as composition [58].

Yet these great strides in the fundamental understanding of the nature of metals and alloys occurred independently of, and indeed almost oblivious to, contemporaneous advances in practical metallurgy. While the chemistry of steel was being developed in Sweden and France in the 18th century, practical innovations in furnace design and operation and new methods of refining, consolidating and shaping wrought iron appeared in England. All this came about entirely without benefit of science and yet it was a major factor in the social and economic changes referred to as the Industrial Revolution.

A major step in increasing the production of iron and decreasing its cost was Abraham Darby's solution, in 1709, of the problem that had been worked on for centuries: that of using abundant coal instead of charcoal for smelting purposes. This he did by pre-coking the coal, removing volatile hydrocarbons and sulphur. Charcoal was in short supply and expensive, because of previous deforestation caused both by the needs of smelting itself and to provide land for agriculture. Darby's discovery was based more on a happy accident of nature than any scientific formulations, for both the ore and the coal available in Coalbrookdale, where Darby's iron works existed, were unusually low in the harmful impurities, sulphur and phosphorus.

Equally important was Henry Cort's improvement of the production of wrought iron. He developed the puddling process in which coke-smelted pig iron was oxidized on a large scale in reverberatory furnaces instead of in small batches in the earlier finery hearths, and he combined this with the rolling mill to give an integrated plant for the large-scale, low-cost production of bar iron in a diversity of shapes and sizes. This was in 1784 and it is rightly regarded as one of the chief contributors to the rapid development of industry and changing attitudes in the Industrial Revolution [59].

At about the same time, the English pottery industry was also changing its scale and nature, partly because of new compositions and partly by more consciously applying new chemical knowledge and management techniques. In this, Josiah Wedgwood was an outstanding leader, though he undoubtedly got some inspiration from the scientific work on the continent and reports of the mass production techniques in the great Chinese factories. But, of course, the iron and pottery industries were only one part of a much broader organic change involving marketing techniques (in which Wedgwood himself was a pioneer), transportation with the expanding canal system, power becoming geographically unrestricted through the advent of the steam engine, a new sense of urbanization and a growing middle class.

The next radical change in the iron industry was the making of low-carbon steels in the molten state. Before the 1860's, malleable iron had perforce always been consolidated at temperatures below its melting point, with inevitable heterogeneity in carbon content and entrapment of slag and other inclusions. Tool steel containing about one per cent carbon had been made from about 1740 by melting "blister steel" in a crucible and casting into ingots, but temperatures high enough to melt the low-carbon materials had to await, first, the discovery by Henry Bessemer in England (or William Kelly in America) that the oxidation of the impurities in the pig iron would themselves provide enough heat to melt pure iron and, second (perhaps more important for a century, though much less in the public eye), the development of the efficient open hearth furnace by the Siemens brothers and its adaptation to steelmaking by melting pig iron and ore together, or pig iron and scrap — the latter by the Martins in France [60].

Though he implies otherwise in his autobiography [61], Bessemer did not come to his process through a study of new chemical and physical discoveries. He happened to see the unmelted shell of a pig of cast iron that had been exposed to air while being melted in a reverberatory furnace and this started him thinking about oxidation. The thermal aspect of his process was also not anticipated, and his first experiments on blowing air through molten cast iron were done in crucibles set into furnaces to provide enough external heat. But, of course, he knew enough schoolboy chemistry and physics to realize the significance of what he observed and had the energy needed to develop the process from an observation to a commercial success. His converter became almost a symbol of an age.

Like Darby, however, Bessemer was also the beneficiary of a happy environmental accident. He had ordered some pig iron from a local merchant without any specification and it just happened to be unusually low in sulphur and phosphorus. His first licensees, using a poorer quality of iron, could not produce good steel; he bought back the contracts and employed some first-rate analytical chemists who found out what the trouble was. Moreover, even the best available iron had some residual sulphur which made the metal "hot-short", *i.e.* fragile when hot. This, in turn, was corrected by the addition of manganese which had previously been used in crucible-melted steels but (as Robert Mushet who patented it recognized) was particularly useful in "pneumatic steel" for correcting the effect of oxygen as well as sulphur. When added as high-carbon spiegeleisen, the ferroalloy simultaneously restored the burnt-out carbon to the level desired in the finished steel. None of these represented advanced scientific concepts at the time, yet all would have evolved far more slowly without the foundation of chemical understanding that came out of the 18th century.

The open hearth furnace was a direct result of new thermodynamic thinking, as was the related Cowper stove for efficiently heating the air for the blast furnace, although the invention of the hot blast itself had occurred in 1828 on the basis of a practical hunch. The Martin process was first simply used for melting and was advantageous in that it employed scrap, but combined with Siemens original plan to melt pig iron and ore in refining, it achieved great flexibility. Neither the converter nor the open hearth process could at first remove phosphorus; although an oxidizing slag in the presence of the lime can remove phosphorus, its use was impractical until a refractory for lining the furnace could be found that would withstand the corrosive effect of such a slag at the high temperatures involved. The Thomas invention of the basic process using magnesite or dolomite solved this — and changed the industrial map of Europe by making usable the iron ores of Lorraine. This illustrates the intimate relationship between metallurgy and ceramics; all metallurgical processes are dependent upon the availability of materials to contain them.

The 19th century developments in metallurgy almost all aimed at the more efficient production of materials known for centuries. Chemical theory was helpful to guide improvements, and chemical analysis became essential in the control of both raw materials and processes. By the end of the 19th century, most major metallurgical works had their chemical laboratories and it was through the analytical chemist that a scientific viewpoint found its way into the industry. Moreover, a new outlook on the part of the metallurgist was beginning to take form, by the combination of the engineer's concern with properties, the microscopist's new knowledge of structure and a flurry of new empirical alloy compositions inspired by the increasing demands of the mechanical engineer. The accidental discovery of age hardening in aluminum alloys in 1906 made possible the Zeppelin (with great psychological if not military effect in World War I) and turned metallurgical thought to a new field, dispersion hardening, of great practical importance and even greater theoretical significance [62]. More than anything else, this event revealed the richness of structure on a scale between the atom and the crystal and stimulated studies of composite materials of all kinds.

The Development of Alloy Steels and Ceramic Materials

One of the main metallurgical advances lay in the development of alloy steels. This had become a purposeful objective at the end of the 19th century, for most earlier attempts to improve steel had involved relatively small pieces of metal for cutting tools in which only hardness and wear resistance were needed. To-day's alloy steels, of course, are those in which high strength and reasonable ductility are required throughout the entire section of relatively large machine components or structures, and the role of the alloy is more to control the depth to which quench-hardening is effective than it is to obtain higher hardness.

The industrial use of modern alloy steels starts with Hadfield's high-manganese steel of 1882, soon followed by nickel steels in 1889 (at first for armament) and vanadium steels in 1904. The last were invented in France, improved in England, but most widely used in the United States by Henry Ford. The requirements of the automobile were the principal incentive for the large-scale development of alloy steels, but the studies of them, at first largely empirical, profoundly influenced the growing science of metals by forcing attention to the complicated structural changes that occur during heat treatment.

Changes of materials can interact with society in ever-widening and often invisible ways. The entrée of alloy steels that underlay the automobile and the change in suburban life that came with it is simply one example of the process. A century earlier the whole rhythm of life had been profoundly affected by improved methods of lighting; later came the refractory thoria mantle for the incandescent gas light, which was in turn largely replaced by the incandescent electric lamp; the latter became possible after a search for filament material had yielded first carbon, then tantalum and, finally, drawn tungsten wire of controlled grain size and shape. The incandescent lamp itself has been partly supplanted by fluorescent lamps depending on materials of quite different physics; still more recently lamps using high-pressure sodium vapor in alumina envelopes, resulting from the most advanced ceramic technology, have altered the patterns of crime on city streets.

The development of cutting tools as part of the background of steel technology was mentioned previously. Tools react significantly on all methods of production and even on the selection and design of whatever is being produced. For cutting operations performed by hand, the traditional carbon steel, hardened by quenching and tempering, was adequate. In the middle of the 18th century, the uniformity of carbon steel (though not its quality) was considerably improved by the introduction of

Benjamin Huntsman's method of melting and casting it. His "crucible" steel was originally intended as a better material for watch springs, but once the smiths and toolmakers learned to work with it, it slowly displaced the un-melted steels for most exacting cutting applications. However, such tool steel begins to soften at about 250 °C, a temperature easily reached at the tips of tools in power-driven lathes. Experiments to improve steel by alloying (including some notable experiments by the eminent Faraday in 1819) showed little advantage and did not disclose the greater depth of hardening in alloy steels which today is the major reason for using them. However, this line, beginning with naval armor plate in the 1880's, became industrially important to automobile manufacture around 1900.

Tungsten had been introduced into tool steels by Robert Mushet in 1868. His tool steel contained 9% tungsten and, when given a normal heat treatment, was found to wear much better than ordinary steel. Its use was economical because it needed less frequent grinding, but it did not produce any drastic change in the machine-tool industry. Then, in 1898, Taylor and White, who were systematically studying the factors that affected machine-shop productivity, discovered that an enormous improvement could be derived from quenching a high tungsten steel from a very high temperature. Such steels were able to cut at much higher temperatures than ever before and the lathe was completely redesigned to stand the higher stresses resulting from the removal of metal at a faster rate. An even more spectacular change arose from the introduction of the sintered tungsten carbide tools in the early 1920's. In turn, this intensified scientific interest in sintering mechanisms, and an important new industry came into being — that of powder-metal fabrication (previously only used for tungsten lamp filaments). Yet, the consuming public is largely unaware of such major advances; they experienced it only in the lower cost or higher precision of the final product.

The age-old abrasive shaping process was revolutionized at about the same time as metal cutting. Synthetic abrasives began with silicon carbide as a product of the electric furnace in 1891, culminating in synthetic diamond (which became commercial in the

1960's) and more recently boron nitrides. Modern mass production of precision parts would have been quite impossible without silicon carbide and related materials for grinding wheels, and the new generation of machines that utilize them.

Although ceramics technology did not greatly change during the 19th century, developments in the glass industry paralleled those in metallurgy. The introduction of the regenerative furnace (later adopted as the steelmaker's open hearth furnace) and of glassblowing machines transformed glass from a luxury object to one of common use. And, just as a more scientific approach to alloys replaced the old empiricism in metallurgy, so the intensive study of new glass compositions, carried out mainly in Germany by Ernst Abbe and Otto Schmidt working for the Carl Zeiss Company, gave vastly better materials for optical instruments and chemical apparatus, and laid the groundwork for the many specialized compositions and treatments in use today.

CHAPTER 8. THE NEW SCIENCE OF MATERIALS BASED ON STRUCTURE

Molecular Structure and Polymeric Materials

Modern MSE, however, involves much more than metals and ceramics. Perhaps the most dramatic changes in this century have been in organic materials, and for this we must return to earlier development of chemistry, moving from the simple inorganic molecule of Dalton into organic molecules of far more complicated structure. Simple atomic proportions beautifully explained the composition of homologous series of compounds such as the aliphatic hydrocarbons. Then the fact that organic substances of the same composition could have vastly different properties — isomerism — forced attention to a richer molecular structure, though similar phenomena had been known much earlier in connection with elemental sulphur and carbon. Wöhler's synthesis of urea from inorganic compounds in 1828 was an early important step toward the union of the organic and inorganic worlds in chemistry, but it took a century and a half more before they merged via the study of structure into a common science of materials. The isomerism of tartrates and racemates was discovered by Berzelius in

1830, and Pasteur showed, in 1848, that when crystallized the latter gave two crystal forms that were mirror images of each other and opposite in optical activity [63].

The structure of molecules took on added meaning when the German chemist Kekulé saw that chemical formulae could designate or even model specific arrangements of atoms in the make-up of the molecule, instead of simply listing the number of atoms of each element [64]. His structural formulae for designating the associations of individual atoms in organic compounds gave a precise representation of the molecule. His flash of insight in seeing the ring structure of the benzene molecule as distinct from the linear-chain character of the aliphatic hydrocarbon molecules not only served to distinguish these two great classes of compounds, but it provided a basic concept for understanding the nature of polymers which are so important today. In retrospect, it is curious that the 19th century chemists tended to resist the idea that their formulae represented the real structure of their molecules: this approach was regarded as little more than a notational device. Only toward the end of the century did levels of aggregation beyond that of the simplest molecule begin to be of concern to scientists, and not until those who were concerned with structure at any one level were ready to seek common ground with others could modern MSE begin.

Kekulé's benzene ring diagram soon had application in industry. Just a few years earlier, in 1856, a young British chemist, W. H. Perkin, attempting to make quinine artificially in a laboratory, discovered a purple dye which he named "mauve". This was the first of the synthetic aniline dyes, and represented the beginning of the coal-tar chemical industry. The benzene ring diagram showed the structural nature of these organic molecules and provided guidelines for the discovery and synthesis of new ones. Under the stimulus of Perkin's discovery and others, the natural dyes, such as indigo, were soon replaced by synthetic ones. In the synthetic dye industry, as elaborated in Germany during the last half of the 19th century, we can see a prototype of what was to become one of the basic elements in MSE, namely the coupling together of theory and practice, basic research done with an end-use clearly in mind. Although the

first aniline dye had been discovered in Britain, it was in Germany that research chemists worked in laboratories which were attached to — indeed, were an integral part of — industrial chemical works [65]. The primacy of the German chemical industry from the last quarter of the 19th century through World War II was undoubtedly a direct result of this fruitful coupling of research with production, and the converse effect of industrial activity on the liveliness of the academic laboratories can also be seen. The German dye industry is an early example of the fruitful interaction between laboratory and factory which was later to become one of the major prerequisites of MSE.

Eventually, from this approach came whole new classes of synthetic organic materials: the plastics. Modern plastics date essentially from the development by Leo Baekland, in 1909, of phenol–formaldehyde compositions which can be molded into any shape and hardened through molecular cross-linking by heating under pressure. This precipitated an active period of scientific study of the synthesis and behavior of large molecules (both aiding and being aided by biochemical studies of proteins) and gave rise to the industrial development of inexpensive easily fabricated materials for general use as well as many specially tailored materials in which desirable properties could be uniquely combined. There was, however, a prehistory of polymers in both technology and science before Baekland's great discovery.

Polymers based on natural products had been used for millennia. All natural materials of animal or vegetable origin, such as wood, textile fibers, pitch and bones, are, of course, polymers. Their chemical modification, as in tanning, for example, can be traced back thousands of years. Many of these materials were combined with other substances to reinforce them or to change their properties as in today's composite materials. Natural polymers such as ivory, tortoise shell and bone had been artificially shaped under heat and pressure molding, and rubber had been used in fabrics of various kinds. None, however, was industrially important until the development of the vulcanization process in 1841. Vulcanized rubber and the heat-moldable natural resin from Malaysia called gutta-percha were extensively used as insulators in electri-

cal apparatus. The first moldable totally artificial plastic material was a mixture of cellulose nitrate and camphor, at first called
Parkesine after the metallurgist who developed it (1862) but better known as celluloid.
The first products were molded pretty trin-
kets, but it was soon used for shirt collars and
eventually photographic films and numerous
other objects such as battery cases. It was,
however, dangerously inflammable. Synthetic
fibers did not become commercial until the
advent of cellulose acetate, "artificial silk", in
the 1920's [66].

The background of artificial organic materials in the form of fibers reaches back to suggestions of the great scientists Robert Hooke
and R.A.F. de Réaumur in 1665 and 1710,
respectively, but this did not bear fruit until
the 1850's when nitrocellulose was extruded
into fine threads, already called "artificial
silk". Joseph Swan's work on the development of carbon filaments for electric lamps
led him to make fabrics from artificial fibers
in the 1880's, but commercial production
stems from France. Other means of getting
natural cellulose into fibrous form was via
solution in alkaline copper solutions, a process in connection with which stretch spinning was first used, thereby permitting the
formation of very fine fibers with oriented
molecules (the cellulose acetate process), and
the viscose process, in which cellulose was put
into solution with alkali and carbon disulfide.
The latter was for years the most popular, but
in the late 1940's cellulose-based processes
were largely displaced by the introduction of
synthetic polyester fibers. All these materials
were used for other than textile purposes,
notably the cellulose acetate airplane-wing
"doping" and the base for photographic film.
These developments gave the organic chemists
and manufacturers experience with polymers,
and the public acceptance of pleasant, low-
cost garments made of "rayon" laid the
ground for widespread acceptance of plastic
products in general. Synthetic resins came
into wide usage for reinforcing viscose fibers
and improving the surface characteristics of
fabrics.

The underlying chemistry and physics of
polymers unfolded without much connection
with the older inorganic material science. It
seems certain, however, that in the future, the
basic sciences of metals, ceramics and organic
materials will mutually enrich one another, no
matter how diverse the manufacturing industries may remain. Scientists and engineers in
the plastics industry today work together in
large research laboratories. Their contributions, which are an important part of the
story of the evolving MSE, have led to many
materials — cellophane, nylon, Dacron,
Teflon, synthetic rubber, foam rubber, etc. —
which have entered our daily lives. This experience has also shown that new materials can
be designed for specific applications almost as
easily as machines can be designed on the
basis of the principles of mechanics and
mechanisms.

Crystallography and Microstructure

Crystallography had little relationship to
practical materials until well into the present
century. Its lively development from roots in
the 17th century depended partly on its utility in the classification of minerals and partly
on the attractive elegance of the mathematical
formulation of the external shapes of crystals
and later the theory of crystal lattices and
symmetry groups [67]. Despite brilliant early
insights, notably by Robert Hooke, into the
relation between crystal form and chemical
constitution, the concepts were not formalized until the very end of the 19th century.
The application of even this knowledge to
practical materials was delayed by the curi-
ously slow recognition that it is internal structure rather than external form that makes a
crystal, and that virtually all solid inorganic
matter is composed of irregular nonpoly-
hedral crystal grains packed together. A most
important step was Sorby's establishment of
methods for the microscopic study of rocks.
Then, in 1863 - 64 he revealed the microcrys-
talline structure of iron and steel in which he
identified seven constituents of different
chemical and structural nature which were
responsible for the well-known differences between various forms of ferrous materials.

Twenty-five years later, this began to interact with new chemical knowledge and especially with the growing body of chemical thermodynamics to permit observation and understanding of structural differences on a larger
scale than that at which physicists and
chemists had been working previously. Then,
rather suddenly, the discovery of X-ray diffraction provided a tool for studying basic

interatomic symmetries, and eventually all structural levels were conceptually connected. This discovery by von Laue and his associates in 1912 and particularly the prompt development of the use of X-rays in the study of the crystalline state by the Braggs in England completely altered the attitudes of pure scientists toward materials and gave a framework within which all types of solids can be understood. It did to the physics of solids what the molecule had earlier done to their chemistry.

CHAPTER 9. ENGINEERING ATTITUDES TOWARD MATERIALS IN THE NINETEENTH CENTURY

Mechanical Properties of Materials

It should be noted that studies of the strength of materials during the early part of the 19th century were centered in France, where the Ecole Polytechnique, the famous French engineering school, had been founded in the last decade of the 18th century and where theoretical investigations of both technical and scientific phenomena reached a high mark. Governmental policy fostered not only the foundation of this school but also encouraged its graduates to use a scientific approach to practical problems. In the Department des Ponts et Chaussees and related enterprises, the best theory and the best empirical tests were merged, and contact with practical problems inspired some advanced pure mathematics at the hands of Navier, Poncelet and other [69].

For most of the 19th century, England's contribution to the study of the strength of materials consisted mainly of empirical investigations of the strength of various building materials. William Fairbairn (1789 - 1874), Eaton Hodgkinson (1789 - 1861) and David Kirkaldy (1820 - 1899) carried out tests on beams and other shapes of wrought iron and cast iron, and iron-framed buildings became common. In Germany, engineering schools based upon the French model were founded, but a more practical bent was given to the education and their students mainly took positions in private industry.

The growth of the railroads led to many, primarily empirical, studies of the strength of materials. Fatigue in metals was necessarily studied in connection with railroad and bridge components. An example of the empirical approach employed by British engineers was the fatigue-testing machine (consisting of a rotating eccentric which deflected a bar and then released it suddenly), which led Captain Henry James and Captain Galton to conclude that iron bars will break under repeated loads of only one-third of that needed to break them on a single application.

Several advanced industrial nations had set up material-testing programs or laboratories, and an International Congress for Testing Materials was established. In the United States such official testing had begun with the examination of iron for boilers in 1830 [70] and was extended in the 1850's with emphasis on materials for cannon. A Board for Testing Iron, Steel and Other Metals was appointed by the President in 1875. Its first report issued five years later includes innumerable original tests and a comprehensive study of the state of knowledge on materials, mostly metallic [71]. The aim was limited to the determination of the pertinent properties of materials that were available, carefully characterized by chemical analysis and by a description of the method of manufacture. Nevertheless, these programs and the carefully written specifications under which materials were to be purchased forced an intimate contact between government, manufacturer, engineer and scientist of a type foreshadowing MSE. The properties measured were initially almost entirely the mechanical properties of concern to the engineer and the materials producer, simply aimed to balance these against the requirements of fabrication. In the 1890's, metallurgists were beginning to study microstructure in relation to mechanical properties, and other properties were becoming important, especially in connection with the electrical engineering industry. Another kind of man investigated electrical and magnetic properties of materials for their scientific interest.

The Joining of Science and Engineering in the Field of Materials

In the first two decades of the 20th century, theoretical physicists began to understand the interior of the atom, and developed quantum mechanics which gave a marvelous key to the differences between classes of solids. This interacted nicely with the findings of the new X-ray diffraction techniques, and real materials became a concern of the physicist for the first time. Not, however, until after World War II did solid-state physics become a well-recognized part of either physics or materials science. Then, in addition to ideas and sophisticated instrumentation for structural studies, physicists contributed techniques for measuring properties of materials — magnetic, electrical, thermal and optical properties — whose studies had been previously largely a matter of guesswork.

In the 1920's, metallurgy was already beginning to move from its age-old chemical orientation to consider the properties of materials in terms of both composition and microstructure. Increasingly, the metallurgist found stimulation by working on topics that impinged on physics, to the advantage of both fields. This changing emphasis did not mean that metallurgy became absorbed into physics any more than it had been absorbed into chemistry at an earlier date; instead, the metallurgist had uncovered phenomena which, in a sense, defined problems for both the chemist and the physicist. Nor did the newly forged links with physicists require the metallurgist to lose contact with chemists; rather, the chemical component of MSE will be enriched in the future by the links with the organic traditions of the polymer chemist and the biochemist. By the end of the 1950's, materials science had been transformed into a multidisciplinary activity, utilizing tools, concepts and theories from many different branches of science.

The growth of the scientific technology in the study of materials during the 19th century parallels a similar development in other fields of engineering.

The classic examples usually cited in studies of science–technology relationships in the 19th century are thermodynamics and electricity. In the former case, technology presented problems for science; in the latter, science presented potentialities for technology. The materials field incorporated both. Technology was also drawing closer to science in another way: one of the most important was the notion of the development of engineering "laws" based on precision, quantification and mathematization in the form of semi-empirical equations. "Engineering science" differing from "pure science" in its motivation was carried out by men who occupied positions intermediate between the pure

scientist and the practical engineer [72]. In both instances, objectives were limited to permit the formulation of mathematical relationships, but those of science were self-chosen to be soluble while those of engineering were set by the importance of the need. The engineer could not be satisfied just with understanding something in principle; it had to work, but he could use in his equations many empirically measured coefficients, even of obscure origin. Furthermore, there were many natural phenomena not investigated by scientists but still meaningful to technologists, and so it was necessary for the technologists to conduct their own scientific investigations in some areas in more detail and on more materials than might be needed for the validation of scientific principles.

As technology has become more scientific and mathematical, and as scientists and engineers tend to work together on many problems, the old distinctions between them are disappearing because each absorbs part of the other's viewpoint. In many cases, we must look into the context in which the work is done in order to decide whether it is scientific or technological. For example, the engineer often discovers gaps in basic scientific knowledge which must be filled before his technological task can be completed. The engineer fills the gap by doing what in another context would be called fundamental research, but, because he needs it, it is called applied research [73].

In contrast, scientists often do engineering in the development of their instruments — as in the building of telescopes, in the improvement of high vacuum techniques and the production of high voltages in particle accelerators — and pure science is often conducted by those with practical aims, *e.g.* the basic studies of recrystallization which came out of work on tungsten lamp filaments and the semiconductor research inspired by wartime radar needs. Early in the 19th century, Faraday's work on optical glass was classic (though not industrially fruitful), and E. Schott's research on new glass compositions in the late 1800's was a model of scientific and industrial coupling which gave Germany a virtual monopoly on optical and chemically resistant glasses until World War I forced other countries to copy the pattern [74].

To equate engineering with applied science is an oversimplification; in practice, engineering involves innumerable choices between alternatives which can be neither exactly specified nor computed. The purposes, the methods, and the goals of scientists and technologists remain different, but the two kinds of practitioners have become more understanding of each other's roles and capabilities. Nowhere is this more true than in the field of MSE.

CHAPTER 10. THE NEW SCIENCE OF MATERIALS AND ITS RELATION TO PHYSICS

Solid-State Physics and MSE

The modern technologies of aerospace, nuclear engineering, semiconductors and the like coincided with the development of theoretical and experimental studies of materials which underlay the new and more sophisticated demand. As we have indicated, the new materials concepts had been developing throughout the 19th century and the first half of the 20th century. For example, the growing involvement of physicists in structure-sensitive properties synergized solid-state physics and metallurgy. Theories of deformation, of the nature of intercrystalline boundaries, of transformation mechanisms and many other subjects popular today were advanced and discussed by metallurgists decades before physicists discovered that there was any interest in this scale of matter. But X-ray diffraction inevitably led the physicist into contact with a whole range of solids and made imperfections unavoidably visible. By 1930 there had been postulated several different types of imperfection — and those resulting from gross polycrystalline heterogeneity and various types of mechanical and chemical imperfections within an ostensibly homogeneous single crystal. These models provided satisfactory explanations of many age-old phenomena. An extremely fertile period of interaction between metallurgists and physicists resulted, now fortunately extending to those who work with ceramics and organic materials as well [75].

Perhaps the major conceptual change was the new way in which physicists began to look at matter. Well into the present, if they thought of the structure of matter at all, physicists did so in terms of Daltonian atoms and molecules, finding therein the foundation of the superb kinetic theory of gases and all of the stereological variability they needed. The great physicist von Laue remarked that physics in the 19th century had no need of the concept of the space lattice. His own discovery of X-ray diffraction in 1912 changed all this. It provided an admirable experimental tool for studying atomic positions in crystals and it interacted fruitfully with the new quantum theory of solids. Only the opening up of a route to the even more exciting structure within the nucleus of the atom prevented this from becoming the main concern of physicists. As it happened, it was not until the late 1940's that the new branch of physics, that of the solid state, began to take form and flourish. In the next decades it came to be numerically the most important of the subdisciplines into which physics was dividing as judged by sectional membership in the American Physical Society.

The development of many specialized branches of physics has resulted in some loss of the physicists' universality that they proudly claimed early in this century. Today's physicist cannot possibly be equally in touch with solid-state physics, biophysics, optics, nuclear physics, fluid dynamics, chemical physics, plasma physics, particle physics, high-polymer physics and physics education, to list simply the divisions of the American Physical Society and the associated societies within the American Institute of Physics. Yet, these specialized physicists all proudly claim their allegiance to physics and their professional interests are coherently maintained. In the case of MSE, there is even more diversity than in physics and the sense of coherence is still only rudimentary. Professional concern for all its branches is not instilled in university training and it is not an essential consideration for maintaining status in the profession. Neither a metallurgist nor a polymer chemist nor a solid-state physicist working in the field of MSE tends to think of himself primarily as a materials scientist or engineer. Why is this? The intellectual, the technical and the social needs all seem to favor the formation of a clearly defined profession uniting the disciplines and providing an opportunity for a life's work in the area made particularly rewarding by interactions with others in the whole field.

This difference between the two forms of association represented by physics and MSE appears to lie in history. The diversification of physics occurred by the gradual condensation of the subdisciplines, at first with no sharp boundary, within a pre-existing framework that encompassed them all. Conversely, all of the component parts of MSE, whether scientific, technological or industrial, had existed for centuries without much connection; the new unity has occurred by the joining of previously defined entities rather than in the division of a larger entity into smaller parts. At the present stage of maturity, physics and MSE do not differ much in the structure and relationship of their parts, but the origin of the subdisciplinary divisions with their interfaces and the mechanism of their growth were vastly different. A highly specialized physicist classes himself with other physicists because at an earlier stage physics did include both fields embryonically. Solid-state physicists, polymer chemists, thermodynamicists and designers of processers of materials have not yet had sufficient time to develop emotional attachment to the new realignment which is coming into being as a result of both social and intellectual factors. By its very nature, the formation of a new superstructure is harder to bring about than the progressive differentiation of a unified field into subunits because the former entails greater changes of the units.

The Nature of Structure/Property Relationships

The properties of the materials that we fabricate and use derive only indirectly from the properties of the simpler systems that lend themselves to rigorous treatment by the physicist. The engineering properties mainly characterize large aggregates of atoms and stem from the behavior of electrons and protons within a framework of nuclei arranged in a complex hierarchy of many states of aggregation. By way of analogy, one cannot visualize the Parthenon simply by describing the characteristics of the individual blocks of pentellic marble that went into its construction, still less by analyzing the grain and crystal structure of the marble itself. The Parthenon would not exist without all these but it is far more than an aggregate of crystals, more than a collection of marbles; it is a

structural masterpiece reflecting, even embodying, the spiritual, economic and technological values of a great civilization. To understand a material it is necessary to know the numbers of different kinds of atoms involved, but it is the way these are put together which basically characterizes the material and accounts for the properties that an engineer uses. The main feature of the new approach to the science of materials is recognition of the importance of structural interrelationship, just as on an engineering level it is an awareness of the interrelationship between a given component or device and the larger system in which it is operating; correspondingly on the social level, each family's needs and deeds must fit in with others to make a world of nations [76].

The new approach to the science of materials is based on the recognition of the full complexity of structure and the fact that the properties depend on it. Once this principle was grasped, materials scientists and engineers could apply it to all kinds of materials and find the underlying unity behind the many classes of materials that had in previous times been studied, produced and used in totally separate environments.

Materials science is limited, of course, by the laws of nature but there are enough atoms of different kinds to produce an almost endless diversity for the materials engineer. There are many new complex structures to be discovered and exploited. Materials engineering is more analogous to the geographic discovery of new continents and cultures than it is to the discovery of the principles of gravitation, navigation or meteorology. To be sure, materials engineers have to work within the laws of nature, but they are also at home in areas too complex for exact fundamental theory and have learned to combine basic science and empiricism.

Although this new approach to materials took form first in the field of metallurgy, the principles have meaning for all materials — ceramics, cement, semiconductors and both biological and synthetic organic polymers. It is beginning to influence geology, as in the past geology has influenced it. Composite materials with structures combining two or more of the basic types of materials on a scale greater than the atomic have, perhaps, the greatest future of all. The dominance of crystalline materials is already being challenged.

The new structure–property viewpoint has served to bind together and to enrich the many strands of pure science which interact in the field of MSE. Without this contact, the crystallographer would focus mainly on ideal crystals; with it, he has been made aware of not only the difference between monocrystalline and polycrystalline matter, but also of the whole range of crystalline imperfections. For the first time in history, scientists have been able to contribute to the understanding of structure-sensitive phenomena. Even in 1920, for example, textbooks on the properties of matter completely ignored most useful properties of interest to the metallurgist, and the strength of materials, as taught to the practical engineer, was essentially a simplified form of elasticity theory, once an important part of mathematical physics.

MSE is as useful to those concerned with production as it is to those who wish simply to understand. On the one hand, studies of solidification, deformation and phase changes apply to the processing and structural control of all kinds of material, and on the other, methods of fabrication that have been successfully developed for one material can solve production problems for another. The influence of ceramics on powder metallurgy is a classic example, but note the transfer of metal-shaping and joining techniques to the new polymers and the application of metallurgical thermodynamics, primarily stimulated by the requirements of the steel industry, to the production of other metals.

When science began to be applied to materials technology, it was done so first at the production end, for only here was it economically feasible. The complexity of structure-sensitive properties which were of concern to the user prevented the application of helpful science until quite late. The early materials were general purpose ones, and the consumer, whether an artist or an engineer, selected what he wanted from a small catalogue. Science at first controlled the chemistry of production, the efficiency and reliability of smelting. Not until well into the 20th century did the structure property concept take hold; when it did a common basis was provided not only for iron and nonferrous metals but also for ceramics and, more recently, organic materials within the same body of knowledge. Science not only offered an explanation for the many aspects of properties that had been discovered empirically, but it pointed the route to improvement and even to totally new materials designed with specific properties in mind.

The end-use and the preparation of materials have now been joined in MSE. Indeed, this state of affairs is inherent in the very concept of a materials cycle as illustrated in the frontispiece. No longer is the primary producer's profit dominant, but profit comes from the best analysis of needs and possibilities. The 19th century engineer selected the best material that was available and improved it marginally. The 20th century engineer can state what he wants and has many more options. Although in both cases economics dictate, it is now at least as much end-use economics as production economics.

Diversity and Unity in MSE

Another relevant factor is the closer junction between science and engineering at all levels. Specialization is needed now more than ever before, but it must be in resonant communication. A new level of organization seems to be emerging, with specializations deepening but with enhanced communication between them. Diversity is an essential characteristic of MSE, but there now exists a means of communication. The science of materials, their engineering design and production engineering at both the chemical and mechanical stages are all interrelated; none is in isolation for each affects the other. A new kind of person is necessary to encourage the liaison, a kind of intellectual manager who, knowing something of many fields, makes his contribution by promoting balance among the disciplines and foreseeing areas likely to become limiting. As it happens, each material has its own complex of requirements, for even when using the same basic shaping techniques, the temperature and forces involved and the sensitivity to atmospheric and other contamination are different. Moreover, the availability of special properties means special uses, and the more specialized the material the more the materials engineer must know the effect of all production variables on successful application. One man cannot possibly encompass all aspects with equal detail, but the validity of MSE lies in the recognition that a certain commonality of problems exists.

As one begins to move beyond the established boundaries of any field or subfield, whether that of a scientist, a humanist or an engineer, the effective approach seems to be not only multidisciplinary or interdisciplinary but also hierarchical. Basing his career on deep specialization in one field, a person must understand the structure and communications within the parts that compose his main concern, and, at the same time, he must be aware of the things to which his specialty is only a part: he must look upward (or outward) beyond the friction at disciplinary boundaries to the larger structure that validates them all, as well as downward (or inward) towards the atoms of which all things are composed. This three-level approach has characterized the work of many productive individuals in the past, but it is beginning to be formalized in the field of MSE. This does not in any way supplant the various scientific, technological, economic or social specialisms on which it it touches, but it does make them individually more meaningful by emphasizing the relationships between scales. And perhaps in so doing, it makes a contribution to the understanding of the nature of knowledge itself.

Scientific concepts come about from an analytical understanding of only a part, albeit often the central part, of a real complex phenomenon. The approach usually requires a temporary blindness to some aspect of the rich behavior of nature, which may have stimulated the study in the beginning. A price is paid for each step in understanding. Eventually, however, the excluded aspects, at least if they are real, can be included in a higher synthesis. However, the history of MSE shows that this synthesis is more than the putting together or exact understanding of many parts; it is putting this understanding into a higher, or at least broader, framework which combines experience as well as logic. All levels, all viewpoints must interact and the present tension between the different parts of the materials profession gives ground for hope that new methods of managing this difficult synthesis are beginning to emerge. It is rare for both attitudes of mind to be combined in one individual, but a tolerance, indeed an enjoyment, of opposing points-of-view is one of the things that makes MSE so interesting today.

CHAPTER 11. THE TECHNICAL REVOLUTION OF THE TWENTIETH CENTURY

Organizational Approach to Science and Technology

20th century technology has been characterized by major changes in approach, method and organization. The change in approach is manifested by the merging of science and technology, as already indicated. Change in method includes the introduction of purposeful and systematic attempts to innovate in order to meet specified needs and wants. The change in organization is reflected in the phrase "Research and Development" (R & D), which involves the employment of teams of people representing different disciplines — a phenomenon unique to recent times [77]. Of course, the building of armies, cathedrals, iron works and operas was always a team operation involving the close integration of many diverse skills — intellectual, practical and managerial. The new element in R & D was the bringing together of specialized disciplines from the hitherto separate communities of scientists and engineers into a productive collaboration.

These characteristics of the technological revolution of our times are to be found in different fields. For example, recent advances in agriculture at least match those in MSE, and are characterized by some of the same elements: the application of scientific study to the basic biology (plant genetics and the mechanism of growth), to the chemistry of insecticides and fertilizers, and to the technology of irrigation as well as the harvesting and preservation of agricultural products. Most important was the interaction of all these with each other — and with the economic and practical environment [78].

This technological transformation in the 20th century seems to have been primarily dependent upon the organization of brainpower, *i.e.* knowledge. There are many nations in the world today which remain underdeveloped despite their possessions of vast natural resources, while some materials-poor nations are among the most prosperous. Partly, this is because the latter have undergone industrialization and hence have built up industrial strength in the past, which continues its momentum; but largely it is because they possess know-how, the knowledge which enables them to organize their technology to overcome deficiencies in the utilization of energy or materials. This state-of-mind is stimulated by productive partnerships between people of quite different motives, representing a great variety of disciplines, and associated with many different institutions. This is especially so in MSE.

The union of science and technology characteristic of American technical advance in so many fields has had some spectacular successes in MSE. Indeed, MSE was central to one of the greatest "breakthroughs" of the past quarter century, the development of semiconductors. Previous technology contributed little to this innovation; the first observations came from empirical studies by physicists of the electrical behavior of all available materials in the 19th century. The first commercial utilization of semiconductors (excluding carbon) was the Nernst lamp of 1901; then followed copper oxide rectifiers, silicon-crystal radio receivers, and eventually radar, which was associated with some theoretical progress during World War II. The major advances in both theory and practice were made in 1947 - 49 in an industrial laboratory — the Bell Telephone Laboratory — where the transistor was developed by a combination of theoretical and experimental scientists and technologists, doing everything from the development of special materials through device technology to the most fundamental physics of matter and circuitry [79].

The recent growth of MSE can, in no small measure, be attributed to the increased recognition by industry of the value of physics; this new attitude toward materials has merged well with the qualitative structural approach that had ripened quite independently within the metallurgical profession. The interaction worked both ways: whereas it might be said that the physicists took the lead in semiconductor research, the quantum theory of alloys began as alloying rules developed somewhat empirically by an academic metallurgist, Hume-Rothery, before it became respectable physics [80].

Similarly, chemical thermodynamics inspired extensive investigations of equilibrium diagrams based on thermal and microscopic analysis of alloys. Metallurgists soon found many metastable structures about which thermodynamics had said nothing, and, interacting with engineers, they used the microscope to study the effect of deformation on microstructure. Only much later did such phenomena become part of the purer science, or influence work on other materials such as polymers and ceramics.

The Interaction of Disciplines, Investigators and Institutions in MSE

One hears much these days about the trend toward increased specialization in all fields. This is certainly true of the component parts of MSE and yet the field as a whole has a characteristic which runs counter to this. For although there are many disciplines involved in MSE, it is in their multidisciplinary cohesion that the value lies. MSE by its very nature encourages communication among practitioners of different disciplines; it also encourages people to learn more about auxiliary disciplines; and, most importantly, it demands interaction among basic research, applications and means of production. It is this systems approach which helps distinguish MSE from its individual predecessor disciplines. Although disciplines are still needed, there must be cross-fertilization among disciplines in MSE, and its practitioners must bear the whole in mind while peering more deeply into their separate parts. The common structural principles underlying the properties of various classes of materials make this possible — and, in fact, underlie the fruitful contributions which the different disciplines can make to the understanding and development of materials.

The new approach entails viewing a host of formerly unrelated activities and processes as parts of a larger, integrated whole. It permits today's scientists and technologists to speak of "materials" as well as of steel, glass, paper or concrete. True, each of these has its own — and very old — technology. But the generic concept of materials represents different arrangements of the same fundamental building blocks of nature. The "materials revolution" allows us to decide first what end-use we want and then select or fashion the material to fulfil that need [81].

An important aspect of 20th century technology is a change in the organizational form in which innovation appears and this is particularly the case in MSE. The old idea of separate or individual inventors working in isolated fashion on problems of their own selection has been largely replaced by research and development (R & D) groups working toward a defined objective in an industrial research laboratory, a university laboratory, or a government laboratory, all of them bringing together specialists in different scientific and engineering specialties. This kind of application of science to technology was already visible in the 19th century in the optical-glass industry, in the German dye and pharmaceutical industry, in the development of the telegraph and cable, and in the embryonic electrical industry; but its systematic application on a large scale is a product of the 20th century [82].

The American experience in industrial R & D shows the influence of the competitive forces characteristic of a capitalist economy. At the same time, this industrial utilization of science fostered a degree of cooperation, first between business units themselves and then among various types of business, governmental and private organizations, that expanded and deepened over the course of time.

Included among the institutions carrying on R & D was the university laboratory; it became involved in a variety of external relationships through the consultative activities of its staff members and later through governmental sponsorship of R & D. A substantial part of the latter support was through the medium of interdisciplinary laboratories (IDL's), which became an important vehicle for governmental sponsorship of materials research in the universities.

The Special Position of Metals and Metallurgy in the History of Materials

If, in this historical review, we have overemphasized metals, it is mainly because the history of metals has been more thoroughly explored than that of other materials. This, in turn, is partly a consequence of the fact that it was around metallurgy that the modern science of materials began to appear. There has been no history of building materials, for example, which attempts to explore both the science and the practice. Ceramic materials, with their spread from utilitarian objects to. the greatest works of art, both inspired and benefited from science in the 17th and 18th centuries more than did metallurgy, but the many good histories of ceramics ignore

science in favor of technology, and even the technology attracts only an infinitesimal fraction of the attention paid to ceramics as art forms. Writings on the history of organic polymers are mainly intended to emphasize the work of one man, company, or country. Moreover, there are few histories of the pure sciences themselves which give adequate attention to the continuous flow of practical problems that have come from men working with materials in novel situations. The level of complexity arising from materials interacting with everything that human beings have done and much of what they have thought for more than ten millennia precludes the presentation of a picture that is both accurate and simple, just as the complexity of materials themselves precludes description by a few simple equations.

CHAPTER 12. WORLD WAR II AND THE EVOLUTION OF MATERIALS SCIENCE AND ENGINEERING AS A COHERENT FIELD

Impact of National Security on MSE

The aim and very purpose of all technology is to respond to human needs as defined in some way by society, though, of course, technology also interacts with society to stimulate new expectations and to offer new possibilities for development.

Throughout history, military requirements — either during times of war or in preparation for war — have helped focus and intensify the pressures for materials development. It was quite obvious in World War II that (a) modern industrialized warfare with its insatiable demand for some materials created critical shortages and hence stimulated research for substitute materials and improved processing techniques, and (b) sophisticated weaponry required materials with specialized characteristics which an older and more conventional technology could not provide.

In the U.S., particularly critical were those materials that had to be imported: rubber, mica, quartz and many of the alloying elements for steels. Research on substitutes -- particularly synthetic rubber and the National Emergency steels — provided a dramatic example of the utility of the new science. Furthermore, the acceleration of innovations in jet aircraft, rockets and nuclear energy brought to the fore critical limitations regarding the performance of materials at high temperatures. And the needs of communications, radar and the proximity fuse made everyone aware of semiconductors and precipitated intense activity in the immediate post-war period. The critical needs for materials during World War II thus forced engineers to recognize the importance and broad potentialities of substitutes and caused a heightened sensitivity to the possibilities of developing entirely new materials of radically different properties. At the same time — and perhaps more importantly — the War inspired close cooperation between pure scientists and engineers of many different disciplines, suggesting patterns of effective interdisciplinary research that persisted into peacetime. Only about one out of ten companies using metals in a 1940 survey had a materials department; over half had such departments by the 1960's [83].

Within a few years after World War II, when the U.S. had entered into the Korean War, a national committee — the Paley Commission — was appointed to study the adequacy of materials supply. At that time, the question seemed to center on shortages of already existing materials rather than on the development of new ones. Such shortages were real. As the 1950's began, the U.S. was simultaneously involved in the Korean War, was assisting in the restoration of Europe's industry through the Marshall Plan, was aiding underdeveloped countries and was still meeting the huge pent-up consumer demand following World War II, often with capital plant which had outlived its usefulness and needed to be replaced. Moreover, the concept of national preparedness during the Cold War made it seem essential to stockpile strategic materials and to build up sufficient industrial capacity for future emergencies.

The strategic requirements as America entered the Cold War era caused the Department of Defense to sponsor many investigations into materials with potential for high temperature service, especially the entire family of refractory metals, but including many non-metallic and composite materials. The problems were scientific as well as technological; at high temperatures, problems of oxidation, diffusion, phase change and loss of strength often became paramount. Brittle fracture, stress-corrosion cracking and other means of disastrous failure also attracted theoretical studies. From investigations of clad and composite materials came a new appreciation of heterogeneity on the scale that had been largely ignored since the days when the duplex steel of Damascus inspired so much research in Europe.

New Emphasis on Sophisticated Materials

The advent of Sputnik posed still new challenges for the growing field of MSE. There was sudden need for the development of new materials possessing esoteric qualities for special applications in space. Furthermore, the usual engineering parameters of economy were of secondary consequence, provided the rigid performance requirements of the outer-space environment could be met. The space program also meant that governmental support for advanced new materials came from a civilian agency, the National Aeronautics and Space Administration (NASA), in addition to the Atomic Energy Commission (AEC) and the Department of Defense.

Other sophisticated materials requirements also made themselves felt. The decision to build a supersonic transport gave added urgency to titanium technology, a field that had been heavily supported by the Department of Defense since the late 1950's. Although public opposition prevented the development of an American supersonic transport, titanium remains a strong, corrosion-resistant, high temperature structural material for other uses; much of what has been learned about the basic characteristics of this metal, its alloys and treatment, including rolling, forging, machining and joining, will remain permanently valuable. Likewise, the requirements for turbine blades to withstand operating temperatures several hundred degrees higher than those in existing aircraft engines also prompted much materials research and stretched the very limits of knowledge.

Similarly, as the forefront of nuclear energy application moved from weapon to power, the material limitations broadened. In addition to the need for conventional materials of usual stability, reactors demanded dramatically unusual combinations of properties. Not only was high- or low-neutron absorption at various energies required (a nuclear property completely beyond the concern of the earlier materials professional), but the materials had also to resist radiation damage and corrosive environments under hostile conditions. Especially challenging has been the swelling of nuclear fuel elements and graphite during reactor operation. As long as only thermal (low energy) neutrons were involved, it could be largely controlled by the use of ceramic (uranium oxide) fuel and by dispersion of the uranium in a ductile matrix, but the new generation of breeder reactors using fast neutrons has raised the problem all over again in far more acute form. Fortunately, radiation damage itself is a useful tool in the fundamental studies of materials and the problem has caught the interest of many fundamental scientists to the benefit of knowledge, development and practice.

In brief, new military demands, the requirements of space, and new demands from fields in nuclear energy, missiles, rockets, communications and the like entailed new challenges to many parts of science and technology and often, indeed, they were factors that paced progress. Materials were central to all.

The most advanced technological achievements today require in their materials the presence of some property to an extreme degree, combined with reasonable stability and formability. This is the very opposite of the age-old materials which typically had to serve for many purposes interchangeably.

One of the major industrial achievements of recent times has been the transistor [84]. The transistor was invented before there was any recognition of the uniqueness of MSE as a viable field of science and engineering; MSE cannot claim any credit for originating the transistor, but the transistor can claim some credit for MSE because it focused attention upon the contributions which the interaction of its component disciplines might make to contemporary society. Interestingly enough, the transistor itself is an outcome of advances in fairly "pure" solid-state physics made by Bardeen and Brattain and Shockley, but it could not have come into useful existence without the inspired semi-empirical development of highly technical zone-refining methods to produce silicon crystals of fantastically high purity and controlled impurities. Moreover, the crystals had to be virtually perfect. Most of the subsequent developments in semiconductors were less dependent upon basic physics than they were upon advances in circuitry, in techniques for microshaping, and in the diffusion of impurity elements to change the local behavior of the semiconductor. No longer did the electrical components have to be separately made and laboriously connected. Every step in this development needed intimate consultation among scientists and engineers — indeed, the boundary between the two disappeared. The background of all this lay in classical metallurgical studies of crystal growth, diffusion and oxidation, but it was a new world which required chemical, crystallographic and mechanical precision far outranking anything previously experienced.

Following the transistor, other devices using semiconductors proliferated. Though previously used in photocells and rectifiers on a small scale, the enhanced theory and sophisticated experience enabled far broader applications. New photoconductors gave birth to a vast array of electrostatic photocopying machines and to devices for seeing in the dark. There are hints that semiconducting surfaces may substitute for the conventional silver-based chemically developed photographic film, itself in its development a marvel of interaction between physical and chemical research and purposeful industrial development.

The laser, so pregnant with possibilities in many fields, is an example of a discovery prompted by intellectual curiosity being rapidly developed by purposeful engineering, both needing and yielding physical insight at every stage.

A much earlier example was the development of hard and soft magnetic materials. The introduction of silicon iron for transformer cores in the early 1900's had a spectacular effect in cutting power losses in electrical systems [85]. As the domain theory of ferromagnetism was developed, even softer materials appeared for communication devices, and at the other extreme there came magnets of strength and stability orders of magnitude better than the older steel or lodestone magnets.

Purposeful Coupling of MSE to Societal Needs

The factor most responsible for the almost explosive change of knowledge and technical capacity in these materials-related areas is the conscious interaction among scientists and engineers. In all of these cases, there was some background of existing knowledge of the materials (sometimes acquired in the academic physics laboratory), but the large-scale applications arose from specifically directed activity based on new theory and constantly requiring new techniques for realization. In the first half of the 20th century, the electrical industry made or inspired almost all the new materials other than steel and aluminum.

A recent example of a spectacularly new use of old material is that of plastic composites in ablative nose cones, without which space vehicles could not safely re-enter the earth's atmosphere. The first search for materials to dissipate the frictional heat was directed toward refractory metals and ceramics; the solution came unexpectedly from plastics, whose decomposition absorbed heat and left behind a continuously renewable porous, insulating, heat-radiating layer of char. Charring had previously been regarded as a thoroughly undesirable characteristic of organic polymeric materials. Now the principle is being applied to other high temperature insulating problems, such as for piping.

New applications for a material can rarely be anticipated for they depend on non-material factors. The properties of any kind of material embody the basic nature of matter, which underlies all things no less than do the laws of gravitation and relativity, but in the present stage of knowledge, real materials combine the basic principles in a way not often predictable. The transfer and development of materials found in a given setting to be appropriate for another is more common than designing them from first principles. Transfer instead of invention is even more frequent in technology than in science. For example, titanium metallurgy was developed intensively with military aircraft applications in mind (benefiting, incidentally, from the experience with zirconium which had proved so useful in nuclear reactors and which had many metallurgical similarities with titanium); as a result, titanium was ready for the Concorde supersonic transport when it was needed. However there is little doubt that the combination of lightness, strength (particularly at high temperatures) and corrosion resistance of titanium will find numerous applications, particularly since its ores are abundant in the earth's crust and it will certainly become cheaper as its presently difficult technology is mastered.

The development of composite materials provides another example of payoff in MSE, and also of some beneficial spillover from military to civilian technology. DoD subsidized much research on glass- and other fiber-reinforced plastics of high strength, low weight and high modulus of elasticity. This began with ballistic missile cases and with structural components of aircraft in mind, and the success in the military applications stimulated the civilian economy for these materials in boats, truck cabs, trailer bodies, geodetic structures: fishing poles, pipe, battery cases, storage tanks and the like. Such high strength, light weight structural materials may some day replace steel and concrete in the multitude of everyday applications.

Perhaps the developments in MSE most familiar to the civilian population are those involving plastics. After all, many of the more sophisticated materials, such as the transistor, although used in everyday devices, are buried inside a "black box". What the public sees, feels and becomes conscious of are the outsides of the "black boxes", which are often made of plastic. Plastics in their many forms, stiff or flexible, transparent or opaque, filmy, fibrous or massive have found their way into every room of the house (especially the kitchen), replacing older materials, usually giving cheaper objects, but perhaps less fragile, more flexible and often more colorful if not more richly decorative than those that they replaced. The variability of the chemistry of the underlying polymeric molecule and the versatility of the fabricating techniques enable materials to be tailored to almost any specific needs.

Since the late 1960's a profound change in societal attitude has forced a new concern upon the technologist and the industrial establishment built upon his work. Through most of history, almost anything that the technologist could do was of some value to the society for, even if unbalanced, it helped to feed and house people, improve their health and facilitate their communication with each other. Today, however, the increased density both of technologies and population makes obvious the necessity for some control within the broader framework of overall societally oriented incentive. This puts new demands on all engineers. No longer can a smelter pour SO_2 freely into the atmosphere. Modern plastics, effective detergents and new ways of packaging products are all fine achievements from the immediate consumer's viewpoint, but they raise many societal problems when the entire material cycle is taken into account. Of course, the engineer has always been accustomed to working toward the balancing of conflicting factors, but in this case, neither he nor anyone else anticipated the broader problems until they had reached considerable magnitude.

The problems that now face the materials engineer are technically soluble if properly tackled. Fuel and raw materials can be produced without destruction of the environment and processes can be developed for the efficient collection and distribution of waste materials of all kinds. The recycling of scrap has been an important part of the metals industry from the beginning and in developing countries is almost complete even today. The emphasis on the direct cost of primary production needs to be supplemented by a broader view. It is a question of seeing the problem as a whole, of designing a system that includes the economics of disposal or recycling as well as the efficient production of a serviceable part.

Newly developed materials enable new things to be done, but they also may do the old ones better or more cheaply. The competition gives life to old industries. Plastics substitute for leather, wood, ceramics and metal in thousands of applications. Electrical transmission cables have always been covered with insulation of some kind; now synthetic polyethylene can not only be applied more easily than the older coatings, but its electrical properties and its resistance to aging are far superior.

It is in this area of substitutions that the next phase of MSE may be most visible, for it ties in with concern over the exhaustion of certain natural resources. Substitutions will enable us to make use of more abundant raw materials than those which are less abundant. However, it must be pointed out that substitution cannot be applied in an unthinking manner, for both short-range and long-range considerations are involved. If more energy is used in providing a substitute or in recycling, this may entail an overall retrogression of en-

vironmental quality. The entire complex of materials resources must be considered; we must protect the materials resources of future generations as well as our own. Perhaps the chief emphasis should be to develop materials which can be recovered and re-used. The refuse of a city is a valuable, if dilute, ore body, whose exploitation is a challenge to MSE.

CHAPTER 13. SOCIETAL CHALLENGES TO MATERIALS SCIENCE AND ENGINEERING

Science and engineering are basic to the quality of life within a nation for present and future generations. The increasing emphasis upon the ecological consequences of contemporary technologies provides another challenge to MSE. Through the development of substitute materials and the creation of new ones, MSE might be a means of insuring the continuation of a highly industrialized society and the extension of its benefits throughout the earth. We must produce and utilize materials in such a way that an ecological balance between social man and his physical environment can be maintained. In this, of course, all fields of science and engineering are encompassed and are dependent upon economic, social and political changes.

While it is true that science and technology have created some of our current problems, many of these are socio-political in origin and antedate the birth of our present industrial civilization. The solution of those problems cannot be resolved by a moratorium on science of by endeavoring to turn back the technological clock. We shall need more science and technology leading to a better understanding of social, environmental and resource interactions. In all this, MSE must certainly play a significant role. At least, MSE provides a powerful example for study of a multidisciplinary effort in a combined academic–governmental–industrial endeavor.

The most advanced MSE has heretofore been applied chiefly to the highly sophisticated requirements of military, aerospace, nuclear energy and electronics. Now it must be expanded to include civilian programs, the development of new materials and new methods of processing the old ones. Will the cooperation of academic–governmental–

industrial efforts be as capable of producing results in the civilian sector?

There are many areas of public concern which will require the attention of the materials community. MSE could now exemplify the newly awakened consciousness of the scientific–technical community toward social concerns. Science and technology represent rational means of coping with the human condition; MSE can make a great contribution, if wisely applied and utilized, to that end.

The contribution of MSE can be of special importance at a time when the public and many members of the scientific community are concerned about "the limits to growth", namely the fear that the world's capacity to support a growing population demanding ever more goods is limited by our store of natural resources, by the cumulative pollution of the environment and by the interaction of these portents of doom. Yet the work of MSE in providing substitutes for natural materials and in developing energy- and resource-saving materials would indicate that the real limits to growth are the limits of substitutability. And the limits of substitutability — as we have learned from the past history of MSE — are the limits of human imagination and ingenuity. We have scarcely begun to probe these limits — for these are the limits of the human mind.

The accelerated advance of MSE during recent decades suggests that scientific and technical limits to growth can usually be overcome. However, unlimited growth of technology *per se* is hardly to be desired; the problem is to achieve viable social organization that can maximize human well-being throughout the world. It is possible that MSE, with its emphasis on functioning structural interplay, may be able to suggest some approaches to the finding of better-balanced social structures.

PART II
MATERIALS SCIENCE AND ENGINEERING AS A MULTIDISCIPLINE

RICHARD S. CLAASSEN

Sandia Laboratories, Albuquerque, N. M. (U.S.A.)

ALAN G. CHYNOWETH

Bell Laboratories, Murray Hill, N. J. (U.S.A.)

CHAPTER 14. INTRODUCTION

We have seen in Part I the earliest origins of materials use by man for aesthetic and practical purposes. Over a long period of time, our knowledge of materials has grown through the interplay of experience and analysis leading to the present mode of activity which we now call *materials science and engineering* (MSE). The historical perspective must necessarily be based to a great extent on archeological findings and the literature.

Part II, which follows, treats MSE from an entirely different perspective. It reports the viewpoint of current practitioners in the field of materials and summarizes the consensus of many participants in discussions on this subject. The definitions and generalizations concerning MSE were tentatively formulated by a panel and then sharpened and refined by extensive discussions within the full committee of COSMAT [86].

We first set the stage for the important concept of the materials cycle and the portion of it which is of primary interest in the present treatment (Chapter 15). Materials science and engineering and materials are then defined as used by us, after which the disciplines comprising MSE and the interactions among them are examined briefly.

Chapter 16 highlights the changing character of materials technology with regard to its role in society and as practiced in various types of industry.

For many, the easiest way to understand the nature and meaning of MSE rests in examples. In Chapter 17, ten case studies have been chosen to illustrate the diversity of the field and to bring out various points which are dis-

cussed in the remainder of Part II. The examples are described in a manner to clarify the characteristics of MSE as we see them, but they are in no way intended to be scholarly surveys of the subject matter. Of course, any decision to select specific examples carries with it the corollary of slighting many investigators who have made equally significant contributions, but the nature of individual contributions turns out to be an important element of MSE. Because MSE has not always been successful, Chapter 17 closes with a brief review of materials-dependent programs which have experienced critical problems or even failure.

Chapter 18 describes some key characteristics of MSE, with its mixture of innovation and response and the associated broad spectrum of science and engineering. The systems approach plays an effective role in such diverse activities involving many traditional disciplines.

We believe that a central element of MSE is cooperative effort among individuals of different disciplines or specializations; thus, the critical significance of coupling between various parts of an MSE program is treated in some depth in Chapter 19.

Our analysis of MSE has particularly important implications for education, as discussed in Chapter 20. An especially difficult problem for the university, which is traditionally structured by disciplines, is to accommodate MSE, which inherently combines various disciplines.

Part II closes with a chapter that emphasizes the continually changing nature of MSE and the evolving opportunities for contributions presented by new, broad, societal goals.

CHAPTER 15. MATERIALS, THE MATERIALS CYCLE, AND THE ROLE OF MATERIALS SCIENCE AND ENGINEERING

Definition of Materials

Materials are ubiquitous, so pervasive that we often take them for granted. Yet they play a central role in much of our daily lives, in practically all manufacturing industries, and in much research and development in the physical and engineering sciences. Materials have a generality comparable with that of energy and information, and the three together comprise nearly all technology. For this discussion, we define *materials as substances having properties which make them useful in machines, structures, devices and products.*

The Materials Cycle

It is useful to depict the materials cycle on a global basis, schematically shown in the frontispiece. The earth is the source of all materials as well as the ultimate repository. Minerals and oils are taken from the earth, and trees and vegetable materials are harvested. Through beneficiation, purification, refining, pulping and other processes, these raw materials are converted into useful industrial materials — metals, chemicals, paper, for example. In subsequent processing, these bulk materials are modified to become engineering materials aimed at meeting performance requirements. The engineering materials are then fashioned by manufacturing processes into shapes and parts which are assembled to make a useful end-product. The product, once its useful life has finished, is eventually returned as waste to the earth, or it undergoes dismantling and materials recovery to provide basic materials to feed into the materials cycle again.

The materials cycle thus divides naturally into two sections: the left-hand (materials supply) side is primarily concerned with obtaining industrial materials, whether from the earth or by reclamation, and from a knowledge viewpoint lies generally within the province of the mineral, earth and forestry technologies; the right-hand (materials consumption) side is primarily concerned with the uses of industrial materials in the manufacture of structures, devices and machines, and their subsequent performance. Again, from the knowledge viewpoint, this side of the cycle is

the main arena for materials science and engineering (MSE), the subject of this paper. However, as the diagram clearly brings out, there is intimate interdependence among all stages of the overall materials cycle. The diagram also portrays the role of recycling — any way which enables materials to keep circulating in the right-hand side of the diagram reduces the demand for new raw materials from the earth in the left-hand side.

Any step taken in any part of the materials cycle may have repercussions elsewhere in the cycle. New paths around the cycle are continually being opened up through researches which lead to new materials, new applications, and thereby new demand and consumption patterns for materials. Furthermore, the materials cycle is not an isolated entity: every stage of the cycle consumes energy and can affect the environment. Increasingly, therefore, it is necessary for the specialist in MSE to consider the effects of technological changes on the complete system of the total materials cycle, including energy consumption and environmental quality.

Definition of Materials Science and Engineering

Many forces have served to shape the multidisciplinary field which has become known as materials science and engineering.

In the first place, MSE has come to be regarded as central to the industrial materials used for machines, devices and structures.

Second, there is growing awareness of the integral role played by materials in the general fabric of society and of the increasingly sophisticated demands made on materials by complex technologies.

Third, this increasing recognition of the importance of materials is coupled with a growing appreciation of the ways in which the societal demands for materials often have an adverse effect on environmental quality.

Fourth, there is new concern (a) that the rate at which the earth is being mined will lead to severe shortages for certain key materials in the foreseeable future, and (b) that industrial processes for minerals and materials are significant consumers of energy.

Fifth, in addition to these external pressures, there are significant forces working within the field itself. There is a growing realization that basic concepts and questions pervade throughout various classes of materials. These intellectual stimuli serve to draw together individuals from many different disciplines in order to achieve, by combining their knowledge and skills, that which none could achieve alone.

Thus, through this combination of external and internal pressures, we see the multidisciplinary field of MSE evolving, forwarding the quest for deeper understanding of materials on the one hand and bringing this scientific endeavor closer to the needs of technology and society generally on the other. We are led, therefore, to propose the following definition: *Materials science and engineering is concerned with the generation and application of knowledge relating the composition, structure, and processing of materials to their properties and uses.*

Materials in MSE

What is meant by "materials" in MSE is clear to anyone until he is asked to define it. Are foods materials? Are fuels? Are drugs? Are bones and muscles? In the broader sense, the answer is yes.

However, a tradition has built up in MSE which focuses on industrial or engineering materials. Hence, food and fuels used in their natural state, and some other categories, are usually excluded. Exclusion is often based on lack of modification of the original properties of the material prior to usage: for example, little processing, substantial tolerance of the product to quality variations, or little durability in use. These boundaries have, of course, been changing with time. But for present purposes, the principal classes of materials falling within the field of MSE are usually covered by the typical labels: ceramics and glass, metals and alloys, plastics, single crystals, and certain natural materials such as wood, stone and sand.

But new ways of categorizing materials are evolving. Because of the spill-over of knowledge and applications from one class of materials into another, the traditional boundaries between classes of materials are becoming increasingly blurred. Instead, it is now common and useful to consider and classify materials according to their function or application — for example, structural, electronic, biomedical, energy-related, etc.

Disciplines and some numbers

The principal disciplines and subdisciplines involved in the multidisciplinary field of MSE are solid-state physics and chemistry, organic chemistry, polymer physics and chemistry, metallurgy and ceramics, and portions of most engineering disciplines. The field embraces parts of synthetic, structural, dynamic and theoretical chemistry; and chemical, mechanical, electrical, electronic, civil, environment, aeronautical, nuclear and biomedical engineering. Many other disciplines and subdisciplines, such as economics and management, interface with these central activities. It is to be emphasized that the disciplinary or subdisciplinary boundaries to the field are indistinct and continually evolving.

Information on the numbers of professionals in the fields is very difficult to obtain, even within a single country. The best available information for the United States is from the COSMAT report, although the basic data are nearly a decade old. The COSMAT Data and Information Panel, under the chairmanship of Robert I. Jaffee, analyzed the 1968 National Register of Scientific and Technical Personnel [87] (often referred to as the Science Register) and the 1969 National Engineers Register [88] to estimate the number of professionals in MSE. The perplexing definitional question of who should be included was answered by a combination of subjective surveys of informed persons and statistical treatment.

About 42 000 scientists in the Science Register were identified as employed in specialties which we define as part of MSE. About 32 000 of those are chemists, with organic chemistry being the largest subfield. Over 9000 scientists are listed as physicists. Of the total group, about 16 500 have doctoral degrees. Half of the latter and three-quarters of the lower-degree levels are employed in business and industry. Multiplying all of the above numbers by 5/3 to account for those not in the Register gives the best available estimate of the total population of materials scientists in the United States at that time (1968).

The conclusions from the Engineers Register were not as straightforward because less detailed information was included in that survey. Furthermore, the Engineers Register comprised only an estimated 30% of all engineers, and only one-in-seven of the actual responses were analyzed (44 000). Keeping these difficulties in mind, an estimate of 40 000 metallurgists and 10 000 ceramists was obtained. About 400 000 professionals in other engineering specialties were found to be engaged in materials work to varying degrees for an equivalent of 200 000 full-time individuals.

In summary, we estimate that there are about 70 000 materials scientists and 250 000 materials engineers, for a full-time equivalent total of 320 000 professionals, active in MSE in the United States. This is a substantial fraction of the approximately 1.8 million scientists and engineers in the United States.

Activities and style

MSE encompasses the entire spectrum of research and development relevant to materials, from basic or curiosity-motivated research done without much thought of its immediate application, to the engineering and design of devices, machines and structures on the basis of available materials data. It can include such fundamental topics as the structure and properties of solidified gases at very low temperatures or the optimization of materials design for high-temperature gas turbines; the developing of an ability to predict the physical properties of plastics from a knowledge of their molecular configurations; or the exploration for suitable catalysts for treating automobile exhausts. MSE also interacts strongly with related activities: education and teaching, commerce and industrial economics, national security and environmental quality. The multidisciplinary nature of the field undoubtedly augments its involvement in a wide range of human concerns and interests.

MSE includes the scientific, rigorous approach to acquiring and applying knowledge as well as the long-standing empirical method. Often the two go hand-in-hand, building on each other — empirical observations of the behavior of materials suggest phenomenological models for their explanation, and these, in turn, often get refined into predictive, analytical models. Both the phenomenological and more rigorous approaches suggest new ways to proceed, say, in endeavoring to optimize desired material properties. Examples of such mixtures of the scientific method and empiricism are the continuing searches for

superconductors with higher transition temperatures, for cheaper and more efficient catalysts and for textured alloys with superior strength-to-weight ratios.

But always, in its most ambitious reaches, MSE relates a fundamental understanding of the behavior of molecules, atoms and electrons to the real world of the performance of devices, structures, machines and products. MSE offers opportunities to combine the deep intellectual challenges and excitement of basic research with the satisfaction of solving real and socially significant problems.

Relevance

Even though the field includes vital activities in basic research not immediately related to applications, MSE as a whole is directly relevant to all of man's activities that depend on machines, devices, or structures. It is involved with the improvement of communications, computers, consumer goods, national defense, energy supply, health services, housing, transportation and so on. Either directly or through the intermediary of these technologies, the field is also relevant to several other key concerns of mankind, particularly environmental quality and the conservation of natural material and energy resources. In sum, the materials field plays an essential role in raising mankind's standard of living and in enhancing economic, social and national security. MSE is, then, a necessary, though by no means sufficient, component for the progress and even survival of mankind. While we cannot always be certain beforehand where MSE will lead us, we do know that, without it, technological advance would slow down and society would have to become reconciled to, or do without, the present state of technology.

Disciplinarity, Interdisciplinarity, Multidisciplinarity

In the materials field, universities have evolved in the past along disciplinary lines — physics, chemistry, metallurgy, ceramics and so on. Similar segmentation is apparent in the industrial sphere, with some industries specializing in metals, others in ceramics, in glass, in chemicals, or in crystalline materials for electronics. In addition, there has tended to be some separation in another direction, between materials science on the one hand, embracing the traditional scientific disciplines, and materials engineering on the other, embracing those parts of the engineering disciplines concerned with developing processes and applications for materials.

Such divisions are practical only when the technical objectives, scientific or engineering, are relatively simple or straightforward. For example, metallurgists may have the requisite knowledge to cope with the problem of developing higher-strength steels in order to lower automobile weight. In such cases, the traditional, disciplinary approach can be adequate for pursuing a problem from the research phase to the production output. But today the trend in technology is towards ever more complex performance requirements, product and device designs, and dependence on very sophisticated knowledge of the physical phenomena that characterize an increasing diversity of materials. The areas of knowledge required to develop, say, an integrated circuit or a biomedical material are not at all coincident with the traditional disciplinary boundaries. It is obvious that many complex technologies call for knowledge and skills that may cut across several disciplines, including science and engineering. Thus, we see an increasing need for interdisciplinary approaches in order to achieve technical objectives.

But the interdisciplinary mode is by no means limited to applied research and development programs. It is also found in basic materials research. The very core of materials science, the relation of properties to structure and composition, implies a need for the combined efforts of physicists, metallurgists and chemists etc. In the past, the physicist has too often made unrealistic assumptions about the composition, purity and quality of the materials of his researches; the metallurgist has too often not understood sufficiently how the underlying physical phenomena exhibited by a solid relate to its structure and composition.

We believe that materials research provides a natural meeting ground for specialists from the various scientific and engineering disciplines, from basic research to applied research, development and engineering, and that the pressure for such interdisciplinary collaboration will grow in the future. It is vital, therefore, to establish the factors that are conducive to effective interdisciplinary materials research.

The field of MSE, broadly speaking, constitutes a multidisciplinary matrix of those disciplines which are related through the structure/property/processes/function/performance linkage of materials. At times, these disciplines are only loosely coupled and interact mainly through the diffusion of knowledge. But frequently, these disciplines are purposefully coupled together in various combinations in order to meet an objective; such groupings are defined as interdisciplinary. It will be shown that the multidiscipline of MSE has proved eminently effective as a medium for many clusters of interdisciplinary activity.

CHAPTER 16. CHANGING CHARACTER OF MATERIALS TECHNOLOGY

Innovation in Materials Science and Engineering

MSE has become a basic instrument in bringing about technological changes. Discoveries of new materials and improvements to old ones — all undergirded by deeper understanding of the intimate relations between the processing, composition and structure of materials on the one hand, together with their properties and function on the other — lead repeatedly to higher performance and efficiency in existing technologies (*e.g.* an improved process for extracting titanium) and to the creation of new ones (*e.g.* silicon crystals and the solid-state electronic industry). By the same token, a breakthrough in understanding the physics and chemistry of biocompatibility of synthetic materials could have dramatic effects on the prosthetics industry.

MSE is both creative and responsive. New insights gained, often unexpectedly, through research on the properties and phenomena exhibited by materials can lead through development and engineering stages to new products and applications of benefit to mankind. But often it is the perception of some potential market or societal need for a product that stimulates the appropriate engineering and development and, in turn, the support of considerable applied and even basic research.

Whether MSE is operating in a creative or a responsive mode, it is having a technological and social impact at a very basic level. Materials as such are usually not very visible to the public that is primarily concerned with end-products and tends to take materials for granted. Yet materials are the working substance of all hardware used in all technologies and are crucial to successful product performance. Between the introduction of materials and the final product, there are often numerous manufacturing stages where extra value is added. Thus, an improved or new material may be decisive in determining the success, usefulness, or social value of a product, even though the cost of the material or the improvement be very modest compared with the total product or social value. In this sense, materials can frequently be said to exert high economic leverage. Color TV has been made possible by the development of special phosphors; synthetic fibers, such as nylon and Dacron, have made drip-dry apparel possible. There are also instances of low leverage in which materials improvements, while useful, do not exert such an enormous change in the end-product or in social patterns; such an example might be the change in steel used for making cans. The National Commission on Materials Policy indicated that non-energy materials and their processing represents about 6 - 7% of the U. S. Gross National Product [89].

Materials are often looked upon as relatively unspecific media which may find their way into a great variety of end-products. New or improved materials may lead to a whole variety of end-products involving widely different industries. For example, fiberglass lends itself for use in pleasure boats, in housing construction and in storage vessels. Hence, materials can be said to have a relatively high degree of proprietary neutrality. One consequence of this situation is that materials research often forms a more neutral, yet broadly applicable, base for governmental support and cooperative ventures among companies than does research in various end-product technologies.

Besides the direct application of MSE to technology, innovation in the field can have important consequences for materials demand, the consumption of energy and the quality of the environment. MSE plays a vital role in meeting man's needs for better transportation equipment, prosthetic devices and the generation, transmission and storage of energy. And by wreaking such technological changes, MSE

can drastically alter the consumption patterns for materials and energy. New materials made from more abundant raw materials can be developed as substitutes for old ones which are made from scarcer or ecologically less desirable raw materials. Indeed, new ways can often be found for performing needed technological functions, *e.g.* transistors have replaced vacuum-tube triodes as basic amplifying elements in electronic circuits and in more recent years integrated circuits have replaced boxes of complex electronic equipment comprising many components. Looking ahead with another example, present work in fusion energy, if successful, could lead to greatly increased demands for lithium. Or again, development of suitable catalysts based on relatively abundant materials could significantly reduce demand for platinum catalysts for treating automobile exhaust gases and for use in chemical processes [90].

As regards energy-consumption patterns, MSE has much to contribute in all phases -- making new forms of generation possible, *e.g.* by finding solutions to the problem of fuel swelling under radiation damage in nuclear reactors [91, 92]; enabling new forms of electrical power distribution, *e.g.* through superconducting or cryogenic transmission lines [93, 94], implementing environmentally acceptable ways to use coal, finding more efficient ways to store energy, *e.g.* through solid electrolytic batteries or thermochemical systems [95], and through finding more efficient ways of using and conserving energy, *e.g.* in materials processing and manufacturing operations and in the development of better thermal insulation materials.

Concerning environmental quality, MSE can play a lead role in finding cleaner materials processes [96, 97], effective uses for waste materials, product materials and designs more acceptable from the consumer viewpoint and in developing instrumentation to monitor and control pollution.

Thus, innovation in *MSE can play a significant part in the economy, in raising the standard of living, in minimizing demands for energy, in improving environmental quality, and in reducing reliance on scarce materials.* In the remainder of this chapter, therefore, a detailed examination will be made of the nature and scope of MSE and the factors that influence its potency as a multidiscipline.

Science-intensive and Experience-based Technologies

Historically, man has made use of materials more-or-less readily available from nature. In this century, however, he has repeatedly demonstrated an ability to synthesize radically new materials to meet increasingly complex and demanding requirements, an ability which so often depends on the latest in scientific knowledge. In fact, so successful has MSE been in recent years that designers and engineers have increasingly come to feel that somehow new materials can ultimately be devised, or old ones modified, to meet all manner of unusual requirements.

In the past, remarkable progress has been made in utilizing materials based on empirical knowledge of their properties and behavior related to their source and subsequent treatment. Many of the important alloys and ceramics were initially developed in this way. This approach is still invaluable and widely practiced. Graphite is a recent example of a material which has solved important problems in missile rocket nozzles and as structural components in nuclear reactors. Yet, the necessary development was achieved by an enlightened empirical approach in a company which was very much material-source oriented. Graphite is a most complex material whose physical properties depend on the nature and processing of raw materials, on the quality of the initial carbon-containing material, on binder pyrolysis and on a variety of processing variables. Hence, the most practical approach to the development of a special graphite to withstand high temperature and pressure was a systematic study of the dependence of properties on processing parameters. The starting point was an initial observation that hot pressing of normal-density carbon yielded a body of high density and high strength. The available science was able to provide only a very general framework for the planning and execution of this program.

This important graphite development also illustrates a governing feature of the historical mode in materials advances. Without a complete science framework and lacking a few broad unifying concepts, the practitioner in graphite development necessarily needed to have access to a very large collection of facts based on past experience with graphite. For that reason, he was material-source oriented and tended to be more affiliated with the material supplier than with the material consumer.

In recent decades, the interest in materials properties has been broadened from that of the supplier to include that of the consumer. In some programs, such as aerospace and the solid-state electronics industry, the material user cannot meet all his objectives with presently existing materials. This, in turn, has often caused the user to become interested in the discovery and development of completely new materials. It has also caused a closer working relationship to be established between the material developer and the material user. Further, the programs which have run into materials limitations of the kind that determine success or failure are, in general, those which are straining for the utmost out of sophisticated science and technology generally. It has, therefore, become natural for the people involved in materials development to utilize scientific contributions when available.

At the same time that the material users have been entering more directly into materials development, the underlying knowledge and understanding in solid-state physics and chemistry have advanced tremendously. These two sciences have evolved several unifying concepts which reach across many classes of materials and now provide common guidance to what seemed previously like disconnected problems in materials development.

Advances of fundamental understanding and the ability to design materials properties to exacting specifications have been most marked in the case of electronic materials. In other areas, however, our level of fundamental understanding is still a long way from enabling us to design materials to withstand new uses and environmental conditions without considerable trial and error. Far from nearing saturation, fundamental understanding of the properties of the vast majority of materials and the consequent ability to tailor new materials to specifications have barely begun.

The term *science-intensive technology* is used here to designate those activities in which specific performance is at a premium and in which the generation of a new fundamental understanding of materials is necessary before the desired performance can be achieved. Thus the descriptor, science-intensive technology or high technology, usually denotes an emerging area where knowledge and practice are changing rapidly and where there has not yet built up a widely based fund of experience and practical knowledge.

A familiar example to illustrate high technology is the space program where it is mandatory that a component must function in the desired manner at the proper time. Because the entire success of an expensive mission may depend upon the proper functioning of this component, it makes sense to expend whatever research and development is required to assure success. The actual cost of the materials going into the component becomes a secondary consideration. Another example is found in nuclear-power reactors. Fuel cladding must be of sufficient integrity to guarantee against hazardous release of radioactive byproducts. In the design and fabrication of the fuel cladding, considerable effort at a sophisticated scientific and engineering level is justified to achieve safety goals. In the solid-state electronics industry, we find another example where highly sophisticated and costly effort on materials is warranted in terms of the overall product value — both the processing of semiconductor material and the assembly into discrete devices or integrated circuits require a degree of control which would be unbelievable in most industrial situations.

The term *experience-based technology*, or low technology, is used to refer to programs which are not science intensive — in other words, which rely on more empirical approaches or which may be highly forgiving of manufacturing and processing variations. Typically, large material quantities are involved so that unit material costs are important. Examples are: the manufacturing of dishes and high-tonnage structural steels; many tires are assembled in traditional ways involving much hard work; conventional approaches prevail in the construction of roads and highways where unit cost is of great importance; and the paper industry continues to use long-standing, empirically derived processes.

Relative Pace of Innovation

There is a familiar pattern in the growth, development and diffusion of a technology. At the birth and in the early stages of a new technology, such as solid-state electronics or nuclear-power reactors, the pace of invention is high and the innovating company or nation may well achieve a commanding position in the market for its new products or services. In this premarketing stage, cost is of secondary importance, or rather it is an administrative decision related to some perception of the eventual pay-off. Later, the inventive pace begins to slacken while, at the same time, other companies or nations with the necessary educational level and technical competence are acquiring the knowledge and skills to catch up. The formerly commanding position of the original innovator is gradually eroded as the relevant technological capability diffuses nationally and internationally. In this stage, where the technology is regarded as becoming mature, commercial advantage is kept by, or passes to, that company or nation that can most effectively minimize production and marketing costs while safeguarding the integrity of the product. Process innovation can then assume more importance than further product innovation.

The early stages of a technology, when the inventive pace is high, are often science intensive and are commonly referred to as *high technology*. It seems that high technologies in which the United States has been in the forefront, such as aerospace, computers and nuclear reactors, have also been generally associated with international trade surpluses for the United States. In the mature stages, the science content of further developments in the technology can then be referred to as experience intensive or *low technology*. Such technologies may be assimilated by developing countries and are more likely to be associated with shifts in trade balance since the latter countries usually enjoy lower costs, primarily through lower labor rates. This may be acceptable for some technologies but not for others critical to national economic and military security. The primary-metals industries in the United States are prime examples of such experience-intensive technologies facing severe foreign competition. Still other technologies, some of which are regarded as high technologies, are moving in the same direction, *e.g.* automobiles, consumer electronics and certain aircraft products.

Because of these trends, nations which depend on high technologies must rely on a rapid inventive pace in order to meet foreign competition and maintain viable domestic industries. We find that MSE can make important contributions both to the creation of new technologies and to the enhanced efficiency of existing ones.

CHAPTER 17. ILLUSTRATIVE EXAMPLES OF MATERIALS SCIENCE AND ENGINEERING

Some Past Achievements

MSE may be described by giving examples of earlier achievements. One way of doing that is provided in Table 1, which is arranged under three column headings — basic research, material or process and examples of applications. This tabulation illustrates the interdependence of these three categories; but by no means should it imply that the initiative for a new development always comes from basic research. The opposite is more typically the case. Occasionally, basic research in materials turns up discoveries which may be of momentous importance, such as the discovery of superconductivity, the theory of transistor action and the discovery of masers and lasers, but more often than not basic research in MSE is stimulated by, and supported because of, its ultimate relevance to practical applications as foreseen by the sponsor if not always by the actual performer.

A second, and perhaps the most meaningful way, to describe MSE is to provide illustrations of past work. We have selected ten examples which we believe were accomplished in the mode of MSE. The examples are as diverse as the broad field of MSE, but each illustrates some of the important aspects which have already been discussed.

TABLE 1

Some achievements in materials science and engineering

Basic research	Material or process	Examples of applications
1 Elemental semiconductors, effects of impurities on conduction properties, impurity chemistry (segregation, alloy systems), crystal-growth studies, dislocations, surface chemistry, etc.	Zone refining, float-zone crystal growth, controlled doping in Czochralski growth, epitaxial growth, controlled alloying, diffusion, oxide masking.	Transistor, integrated circuits, tunnel diodes, charge-coupled devices.
2 Binary compound semiconductors, plus special emphasis on optical properties — luminescence, electroluminescence. Band-structure theory.	Increased control over epitaxial growth — liquid phase epitaxy; gallium arsenide, gallium phosphide, silicon carbide; Group II–Group VI compounds.	Light-emitting diodes, injection lasers, bulk negative-resistance devices.
3 Phase diagram exploration. Properties *vs.* composition.	Ternary and quaternary compound semiconductors.	Solar cells, optoelectronics, nonlinear optical devices.
4 Ferroelectrics; dielectric properties of polar and non-polar crystal lattices. Pyroelectric properties.	Nonlinear optical materials; electro-optic materials, *e.g.* $LiNbO_3$, $LiTaO_3$, $Ba_x Sr_{1-x} NbO_3$, $Ba_x Na_{1-x} NbO_3$, etc.; lead zirconate titanate; ferroelectric polymers.	Optical modulators, deflectors, harmonic generators; parametric oscillators and amplifiers; infrared pyroelectric detectors; microphones; transducers; piezoelectric filters; electrostatic copiers.
5 Phase-equilibria studies under extremes of pressure and temperature.	Synthesis of diamond; boron nitride.	Abrasives, cutting tools.
6 Superconductivity; electrical magnetic and thermodynamic properties of metals at extremely low temperatures; many-body theory; lattice modes; Josephson effect.	New superconductors — high transition temperature, high critical current, *e.g.* β-tungstens; superconducting switches; thin superconducting films.	Superconducting solenoids, for high magnetic fields; ultra-low electromagnetic signal detectors; cryogenic logic; new voltage standard referenced to frequency; Josephson circuits.

7 Magnetic properties of insulating crystals — relating magnetic properties to crystal structure and composition.	Ferrite crystals; garnet crystals.	Microwave devices — circulators isolators; bubble-domain memory and logic devices.
8 Magnetic alloys — relation of magnetic properties to composition, microstructure and deformation.	Grain-oriented silicon–iron; Permalloy; Rememdur; cobalt rare-earth alloys.	Transformer cores; nonlinear magnetic devices — pulse transformers, amplifiers, memories; controlled coercive-force alloys; high coercive-force alloys.
9 Physical chemistry of hydrothermal growth process.	Synthetic quartz.	Frequency standards and filters.
10 Theory of sintering; basic annealing studies.	Powder metallurgy; high density, transparent ceramics; high strength alloys.	Lamp envelopes; light weight armor; precision parts; ceramic turbine blades.
11 Magnetic properties of polycrystalline ferrites.	Hard and soft magnetic ferrites.	Computer core memories (soft); magnetic door latches (hard); deflection cores for TV tubes; high voltage transformer cores.
12 Surface chemistry; oxidation-reduction reactions; electrochemistry — electrode kinetics.	Catalysis; surface modification.	Batteries; hydrogen–oxygen fuel cells; corrosion prevention.
13 Rheology; physical chemistry of surfaces; synthesis of compounds.	Structural adhesive; pressure-sensitive adhesives.	Joining techniques; Scotch tape, epoxy cements; moldings and castings.
14 Solidification studies: transparent analogues.	Metal fiber spinning, rheocasting; edge-defined film-fed growth; directional solidification, better continuous casting; amorphous materials.	Steel wire; aluminum die castings; solar cells; turbine blades; magneto-resistance devices; anisotropic magnets; premium castings.
15 High temperature phase equilibria.	Chemistry of steelmaking; basic oxygen process; protective coatings.	Cheaper steelmaking; longer-life furnace linings; corrosion-resistant components.
16 Radiation effects in crystals.	Ion implantation.	Integrated-circuit technology.
17 Radiation effects in polymers.	Polymer cross-linking or scission radiation-sensitive polymers.	Heat-shrinkable polyethylene and polyvinylchloride; photoresists; radiation dosimeters.
18 Thermal expansion of ceramics; nucleation and phase precipitation.	Glass ceramics.	Ovenware; catalytic substrates; low expansion mirrors.
19 Thermodynamics of phase diagrams, chemical processes; particle strengthening.	Dispersion alloys — internally oxidized particles to strengthen materials, thoria-dispersed nickel, dispersion-hardened Al, Cu, Ag; spinodal decomposition; 2-phase polymer systems.	Aerospace alloys; aluminum conductor cables; copper conductors, electrical contacts; high-strength and magnetic alloys; moldable and castable elastomers.
20 Structural stability in high radiation flux.	Fuel cladding; radiation-stable polymers for electrical insulation.	Nuclear power.
21 Fracture studies; fatigue, dislocation theory.	Non-destructive testing techniques; computer-aided metals design; high fracture-toughness materials.	Wide range of structure, high performance applications; failure prediction techniques.
22 Deformation theory for polycrystalline solids; annealing behavior; precipitation hardening; recrystallization; superplasticity.	Hydrostatic extrusion and forming; textured materials; superplastic forming; shape and memory effect; new alloys; Al-based and Ni-based	Shapes and parts; transformer steel; Alnico magnets; spring metals; heat-shrinkable metals; aerospace applications; turbine blades; razor

	precipitation hardening; precipitation-hardened steel.	blades; quality cutlery.
23 Spectroscopy of transparent materials.	Lasers; optical fibers and films.	Optical communications and data processing; ranging for ordnance and surveying; machining.
24 High temperature erosion studies; pyrolysis.	Firebricks; weather resistance; ablation; carbon-fiber processing from polymer precursor.	Reinforced plastic nose cones and ablation shields; furnace linings; constructional materials.
25 Ion exchange and diffusion in glasses.	Surface-strengthened glass.	Strong fibers; optical fibers; aircraft windshields.
26 Crystal growth.	Vapor–liquid–solid growth processes.	Cold cathodes.
27 Heterogeneous catalysis.	Electroless deposition.	Electroless coatings of Au, Co, Cu, Ni, Sn, Al, Mg, Ti.
28 Orientation of macromolecular chains.	Spinning of fibers from melts and solutions: rayon, nylon, acrylins, polyesters, aramides.	Synthetic textiles; tire cords.

Case Studies of Materials Science and Engineering

Heatshield design*

The design of a heatshield for an aerospace reentry system provides an excellent example of the integral role of MSE in advanced engineering programs. The primary purpose of the heatshield is to provide thermal protection from the reentry environment. From the first definition of heatshield requirements to synthesis of a system to meet these requirements, support efforts in the areas of orbital mechanics, aerodynamics, trajectory analysis, heat transfer, physics, chemistry, materials science, experimental testing and manufacturing techniques are essential. The system design problems related to manned earth orbital or lunar return reentry (Apollo) and unmanned planetary return (SNAP — radio isotopic heat source) are used here to illustrate the close relationships between material design and other aspects of the program.

Perhaps the single most important parameter which determines the reentry environment is the vehicle ballistic coefficient or weight-to-drag area ratio. Examination of simplified equations of motion shows functional relationships between the ballistic coefficient and velocity, altitude of maximum deceleration, altitude of maximum heating rate, and maximum heating rate. For a fixed reentry velocity and angle, an increase in ballistic coefficient produces higher heating rates and increased total integrated heat. The value of maximum deceleration is not strongly dependent on ballistic coefficient, but rather depends on reentry velocity and angle, with increase in velocity and angle yielding an increase in deceleration loads. It is apparent that selection of a low ballistic-coefficient vehicle leads to a reduction in the overall thermal environment to be experienced. The magnitude of vehicle "local" thermal environments is further influenced by vehicle size and configurations and will be discussed later. The major reentry environmental parameters for vehicles entering the earth's atmosphere are the convective heating rate, total heat-load or integrated convective heating rate, total pressure and vehicle deceleration. Representative values of these parameters for several systems are shown in Table 2. It is these parameters which set the heatshield design and material-property requirements.

It was recognized in the Apollo program that a relatively blunt vehicle would be required to minimize convective heating, but some concern was expressed over the magnitude of nonequilibrium radiation from the shock layer to the body. Estimates made in this time period indicated that nonequilibrium radiation might be orders of magnitude higher than equilibrium radiation and could be a dominant factor in entry heating. Further theoretical studies and experimental work conducted in shock tubes and light gas guns dispelled this concern and showed that for the Apollo application the command module configuration should be designed to provide minimum convective heating. However, lunar ballistic reentry allowed entry in a narrow corridor only seven miles wide. To widen the corridor, a moderately lifting vehicle was suggested, and undershoot trajectories limited to 20 g for crew survival and overshoot trajectories (5000 nm range) for maximum heat load were studied. Therefore, the manned lunar mission, entry corridor convective heating and deceleration limits defined the major design requirements for reentry of the Apollo command module.

By the mid 1960's, studies had shown that the previously used burn-up approach during reentry of SNAP devices was unsafe because radioactive material could be dispersed in the earth's atmosphere. It was

---

*The information for this account was furnished by R. C. Maydew, Sandia Laboratories.

TABLE 2

Typical reentry environment parameters for reentry vehicles entering the earth's atmosphere

Mission	Reference heating rate, $\dot{q}_{Ref_{max}}$ (BTU ft$^{-3/2}$)	Total integrated heat, $\int \dot{q}_{Ref}$ (BTU ft$^{-3/2}$)	Vehicle maximum pressure, P_{T_2} (atm)	Vehicle maximum deceleration (g)
SNAP 27 preorbital	300	8500	1.4	25.0
SNAP 27 earth orbital	100	42 000	0.17	7.0
SNAP 27 lunar return (6.25°)	500	25 000	0.37	14.0
SNAP 27 lunar return (38°)	600	9000	5.4	200.0
Pioneer Jupiter return (9°)	1500	40 500	2.0	45.0
Apollo (entry design limits)	700	42 000	1.5	20.0

then decided to convert the fuel capsule in the Nimbus-B/SNAP-19 generator system from a metallic burn-up capsule to a graphite-heatshield protected system to provide intact reentry.

It is evident from the previous description of the reentry environment and heatshield design problems that synthesis of materials tailored to meet the design requirements was essential. The specific contribution of the materials expert within the ablation heatshield development team might be exemplified by a brief description of the process of materials selection and the tools which are used. The materials specialist is involved in the physical phenomena and chemical interactions between the reentry environment and an ablative material. Current ablation theory states that an ablation material can reject heat in the following ways:

(a) by warming from some temperature to the decomposition point and above;

(b) by decomposing into small fragments (high decomposition energy);

(c) by tailoring the fragments to have high specific heats in order to carry off a large amount of heat; and

(d) by forming an outside layer of porous char which reradiates some of the heat energy away and which adds additional heat to the gaseous fragments which percolate through it.

In addition to these heat-rejection mechanisms, the ablator insulates the interior of the vehicle from the high-temperature surface. Depending upon the reentry environment and proposed application, the materials engineer, whose role is to assess the practicality of tailoring a material to fit a set of desired attributes, will select one or more of the four ablation mechanisms to be the predominant method of heat removal.

To make the first-cut choice of an ablator, the materials specialist uses expertise from several disciplines: organic and physical chemistry, physics, mechanics and polymer chemistry. An example will illustrate the process more fully.

Assume that the guidance from other parts of the team indicates that the material must, as one of several requirements, have a high decomposition energy. The materials expert would then begin to optimize materials for each part of the requirement,

after which he would run a series of parametric studies to obtain an ablator.

To address the requirement of high decomposition energy, chemical theory would first direct him to the most thermally stable organic molecules, as follows: chemical-bond thermodynamics shows that, in organics, π bonds are stronger than σ bonds (142 *versus* 80 kcal mol^{-1}). In addition, the theory of quantum-mechanical resonance of conjugated π bonds indicates that additional stability can be obtained by delocalization of as many π bonding electrons as possible. This results in the selection of aromatic hydrocarbons with structure as near to that of graphite as possible.

The next step is to incorporate this molecular structure in a usable material. Since graphite is not a workable material, other smaller aromatic molecules are considered (benzene, toluene, biphenyl, phenol, etc.). These molecules alone are not appropriate; therefore, they must be made into a usable solid, a polymer. Chemical-bond thermodynamics and resonance theory again provide the direction for the kind of joining required, all π bonds. However, polymer trade-off studies have shown that the best system would be to use σ carbon-to-carbon bonds with as few bonds as possible in the joining link and as many joining links as possible.

At this point, a decision must be made as to the kind of polymer desired, a thermoplastic, a rubber, or a thermoset material. Polymer thermal-decomposition studies show that, in general, the higher the crosslinking, the more thermally stable the polymer. Also, from mechanical considerations of heatshield strength a crosslinked material is required. When these considerations are combined with a knowledge of organic reactions, a reaction is selected which will allow a first-cut material to be made. This reaction is a condensation reaction of formaldehyde with phenol (phenolic polymer) to yield an aromatic structure joined together by two σ carbon–carbon bonds in each link. In addition, since phenol has a possibility of three reaction sites, two ortho and one para to the hydroxyl, the degree of crosslinking can be varied to suit the requirements.

Condensation reactions usually yield by-products, such as small molecules which are removed in gaseous form. When large test samples are required, the diffusion times for these gases to be swept from the system become prohibitively long. If heat and pressure are used to speed the diffusion and condensation reaction, large material defects, bubbles and voids, will occur. A compromise which allows the preparation of good samples in spite of the off-gassing is obtained from the knowledge that, first, some polymerization reactions can be carried part way to completion, stopped and then restarted. This allows the removal of an appreciable amount of the gas before sample synthesis is attempted. Parametric studies are conducted to optimize the amount of prereaction. Second, diffusion studies have shown that gaseous diffusion is several orders of magnitude larger along polymer interfaces than through a bulk polymer. Thus, any filler which would give a continuous interface would enhance the removal of the gas. With this approach, blocks of material can be made for testing.

In the manner just described, also addressed in the MSE mode are: fiber technology, char technology, layup technology, ablation–reaction chemistry, adhesion, physics of transpiration cooling, all to optimize each desired attribute. Then, parametric studies are used to distill the mixture of best attributes into one best ablator for a given application.

Thermal properties, including calorimetry for specific heat and enthalpy, are needed to determine the amount of energy required to warm the material to the decomposition point. Thermal conductivity of the virgin material and the char is needed to indicate the velocity of the heating front. Thermal expansion and thermal shock resistance are required to determine compatibility with the substructure as well as the structural integrity of the virgin ablator and the char during the service conditions.

Mechanical properties include static and dynamic loading at elevated temperatures on both the virgin material and the char. These data allow stress analysis in order to make predictions of the performance of the heatshield during flight and other loadings. In addition, early in the study, certain of the mechanical tests would be used as screening methods to determine which of several fibers (*e.g.* carbon, quartz, or nylon) available through previous research, would be the best choice in this application. Several generations of material are required to optimize and trade-off the many requirements.

Preliminary ablation testing must be made to help screen candidate composite formulations by visual postmortems, determination of material-loss and energy absorbed/unit material, and finally proof testing under conditions as near those of the flight as possible. The selected shield or test article must then be instrumented with sensors for heat, material removal, char depth, etc., measurements to pass final acceptance (usually in concert with a heat-transport team member).

The synthesis of prototypes and actual heatshields would be the next requirement of the materials man. He must include in his considerations such things as: How should any reinforcing fibers or cloth matrix be used to produce the correct mechanical properties? How should the material be configured? How should the ablation shield be attached to the substructure?

Has the weight allotment been met? Can better physical geometries be found through parametric computer studies? Can the shield be made more reliable by computer control of the fabrication equipment?

In conclusion, one must remember that the solutions to most problems are never black or white, and neither is the choice of an ablator without its trade-offs. To obtain an essential condition, such as low back-surface temperature, other characteristics, such as char formation, will degrade. These trade-off studies, along with testing, theories of ablation, decomposition, polymer synthesis and composite synthesis (mechanical properties), are also embodied in MSE.

Material characterization is carried out with laboratory samples sufficiently large to measure chemical and physical properties, bearing in mind that, as an example, the mechanical characteristics of a reinforced polymeric system can be significantly affected by its geometry. Thermogravimetric and differential thermal analyses, as well as gas chromatography and mass spectrometry, are used to determine the decomposition energy, the amount of char and the gaseous species formed during ablation. These tests will also show the compatibility between the organic and the fiber and substructure. At this point, additional molecular tailoring may be done to enhance a property further. Microscopy and X-ray diffraction are used to identify structure and structural changes of both the virgin material and the subsequent char.

The importance of MSE in the heatshield design area is further exemplified when one considers the serious problem of variability of material properties in materials supplied by commercial vendors. Vehicle design considerations and safety factors based on minimum material properties lead to conservative designs, a luxury which may not be tolerated in extreme reentry environments. As reentry environments become more severe, it is through the work of MSE under controlled laboratory conditions that new materials will be created to satisfy the demand for ever-increasing performance of ablative heatshield materials.

During the winter and spring of 1960 - 1961, several materials were considered for the lunar return mission, including phenolic nylon, epoxy ablators and a silica-fiber-reinforced material. Phenolic nylon tiles over a supporting honeycomb-sandwich structure of stainless steel was the approach finally selected. The main design requirements for the ablator were that it limit the temperature at the ablator–steel interface to 600 °F during entry, that it be compatible with the steel substructure, and that it survive thermal cycling from −250 °F to +250 °F prior to entry. In addition, it had to provide boost thermal protection and withstand micrometeoroid, vacuum and ultraviolet exposure.

By contrast, the materials chosen for the isotopic heat source were required to have high steady-state surface temperature capabilities (900 °F), resistance to high heating rates and the capability to limit the thermal input to the vehicle during entry. These properties were exhibited by POCO and ATJ-S, a highly graphitized carbonaceous material of high density. In addition, such bulk graphites displayed acceptable ablation rates (thermochemical) and thermal stress resistance over the range of pressure, temperature, and enthalpy experienced.

Discovery of the Transistor*

The transistor story emphasizes the changing nature of a materials research and development program with time. In its early phases, only fundamental understanding of the nature of electrical conduction in semiconductors was involved. The motivation or "application" was stated only in a most general way, but there was a perceived need to replace vacuum tubes in communications circuitry. This program substantially increased understanding of the solid state, but it was necessarily built on much basic work in physics and chemistry which had been completed in earlier decades. Although the present account emphasizes the research effort leading to device feasibility, with time the emphasis naturally shifted from research on phenomena to the engineering aspects of design and manufacture. Movement of personnel from research to development played an important role. This program provides a particularly strong example of close coupling between basic research and engineering. The solid-state industry which has grown out of the original transistor work is the archetype of a science-intensive industry and creative materials research and density. The transistor story also illustrates the cardinal importance of proper intellectual and working environment for innovative materials research and density. A sense of direction was provided by the management in a sufficiently general way so that individual creativity and insight were encouraged, and yet was sufficiently definite to arouse the enthusiasm and dedication of the experts involved. Leadership across the spectrum of these programs fell naturally on those able to span intellectually and motivationally the full scope of the overall effort.

As expressed in its corporate goal, the Bell Telephone System has the obligation of meeting one of the major needs of society, namely, "To provide the best communications service at the lowest possible cost consistent with financial health". This goal must be met in ways which enable the Bell System to compete with other industries for the necessary capital and other financing. Thus, Bell Telephone Laboratories is a research and development organization coupled to an industry required to meet a social need in a financially (competitive) efficient manner. From the management point of view, this immediately translates into having continually to find ways of improving the technology of communications. In this way the Bell System can meet the external pressures of social demands for better (*i.e.* more diverse and reliable, cheaper, quicker, etc.) communications and the internal corporate pressures for competing in the market (*i.e.* lowering costs, installing equipment more quickly, achieving higher reliability, etc.).

---

*Based on published documents and on archival material at Bell Telephone Laboratories, Inc.

In the mid-1930's, Mervin Kelly, then Executive Vice President of BTL, found himself wondering about the limitations of relay and electron-tube technologies. It was his job to look ahead 10 - 15 years. He reasoned that, if one had to rely only on tube or relay improvements, the Bell System would not be able to afford the larger, more complex and more capable communications systems that would be needed in the future. There were simply too many intrinsic physical limitations in both electron-tube and relay technologies. Relays were inexpensive and reliable, but far too slow to perform the more challenging functions of the new switching systems needed. They could work for digital functions, such as low-speed logic and memory, but could not be applied to the many other analogue and high speed digital functions that a complete future communications system would require. However, electron tubes were very fast: all they had to do was move electrons in vacuum in response to information signals. They could perform both high speed digital and analogue functions. But electron tubes extracted a large economic penalty. The hot cathode consumed power in wasteful quantities and the failure rates of tubes were too high to allow the use of large numbers of tubes per system. Thus, operating costs and maintenance expense would prohibit the applications of electron tubes to the much larger, more complex switching and multichannel transmission systems that were needed. And, of course, tubes were absolutely ruled out of telephone apparatus by their shortcomings on power and reliability as well as size. So Kelly concluded that a new component technology was needed. It must be fast and versatile like the tube, but it must be efficient in its use of power. Above all, it must be many orders of magnitude more reliable than tubes if it were to be applied to the much larger, more complex systems of the future.

The outbreak of World War II made it necessary to shelve plans to follow this train of thought with action; but after the war Kelly returned to the problem. When he told his research people what concerned him, they told him of the current state of understanding in many relevant areas of physical electronics such as cold-cathode gas-discharge phenomena, magnetics, electroluminescence and conduction of electricity in such solids as metals, insulators and semiconductors. One by one, most of the possibilities were eliminated because of one limitation or another: insufficient speed, too many restrictions in functions, or the judgment that sufficient understanding to achieve application could not be developed soon enough. The search narrowed down to solids, such as insulators, metals, or semiconductors. In a conductor there are many electrons, but not enough of the basic science was known to control them. In an insulator, there are very few electrons and not much to be done about it without altering the basic material structure. But in a semiconductor, there can be many electrons or not, depending upon what one does to the semiconductor with impurities, heat, light, or electric stimuli. For many years, empirically discovered semiconductor devices had been used in electrical technology, such as copper oxide and silicon rectifiers, and resistors whose characteristics could be controlled in response to thermal, light and electric signals. Researchers were trying to understand why a semiconductor behaves as it does. How does it differ from metals and insulators? Why is its resistance so sensitive to impurities, imperfections and various forms of energy? Wilson and Mott had studied these problems in England, Davidoff and Joffe in Russia, Schottky in Germany and Lark-Horowitz at Purdue University, just as people had done at Bell Laboratories. There was indeed a large and impressive body of theoretical and experimental work at hand. Shockley and Fisk concluded that the most promising and relevant area in which one might look for new electronic phenomena for amplification lay in semiconductors — if one could understand the basic physical and material science.

The best theory in those early days did not explain the relation between structure and function in any quantitative way for copper oxide or germanium rectifiers. In fact, it would not even predict accurately the direction of rectification. But certain promising elements and aims were at hand: it was known that the need was to produce and control the flow of electrons such that the basic atomic structure of matter would not be altered; otherwise the same kind of wear-out problem would result as with hot cathodes. It was known that there could be many electrons in semiconductors at room temperature and that they could be moved very fast without altering the basic material structure. For example, silicon and germanium rectifiers would behave as very fast electronic switches, and other similar devices would also respond to heat- and light-signal energy. So the real question became, "Can we understand, and thereby learn how to generate and control economically, the electrons in semiconductors?" The decision to do research on semiconductors was finally made; it was signaled by Kelly, but only Fisk, Shockley and their fellow researchers knew the scientific potential. Together, managers and scientists formed a synapse between a broad long-term system need and a possible answer in a relevant area of science. They had no concrete ideas on what form any new electronic device might take, but they had faith that basic understanding of semiconductors could lead to the synthesis of a new electronic device.

Nobody could put a quantitative value on the probability of success or on how long it would take to succeed. All that could be said was that there was an excellent chance of achieving understanding because the quantum physics of solids was mature and powerful; at least, understanding of the simplest elemental semiconductor, such as germanium, should result. This was why work started with germanium and later turned to silicon, despite the fact that more complex semiconductors, such as copper oxide and silicon carbide, were in much larger commercial use as empirically developed devices. The simplest material was picked because basic understanding was being sought which, it was hoped, would in turn lead to control and application based on such understanding.

The decision to intensify research into semiconductors, which were originally discovered by Faraday in 1833, reflected awareness of the intriguing variety of properties of these materials that had been discovered in the preceding hundred years as well as their use already in a number of rudimentary devices. These basic discoveries and the development of a formal understanding of them were very much the inspired work of individuals whom we would nowadays call solid-state physicists, for example:

1839 Becquerel discovers photovoltage between semiconductor and electrolyte;

1873 Smith discovers photoconductivity in selenium;

1874 Braun discovers non-ohmic behavior at metal sulfide contacts; Schuster discovers non-ohmic behavior at copper-tarnished copper contacts;

1876 Adams and Day make barrier-layer photoelement with selenium;

1879 Hall effect discovered, indicating some metals have positive carriers;

1883 Fritts makes first large-area dry rectifier with selenium;

1904 Various discoveries that point contacts on galena, silicon carbide, tellurium and silicon make good detectors of radio waves. (Silicon was found to be the most stable, and though the rectification mechanism was not known, it was shown *not* to be thermal.)

We see from the above list that some basic properties of semiconductors and particularly the rectifying properties of contacts were established as far back as 1883. By 1904 it had been shown that such contacts could be used for detecting radio waves but the suitability of vacuum tubes at that time for such applications lessened or delayed interest in semiconductor effects.

However, in the 1920's, various commercial semiconductor devices started making their appearance including the copper oxide and selenium rectifiers and selenium photocells. These commercial devices created a demand for a better understanding of how they worked, so that through the 1920's and 1930's much experimental research went into the properties of semiconductors. Some of the best controlled studies were made in Germany by Gudden and Pohl on the related materials (generally more insulators than semiconductors) alkali halides; their progress, it was clear, was considerably aided by the fact that such materials could be prepared fairly readily in single-crystal form. As a result of such researches, it was established that rectification and photovoltages were body properties. In the meantime, theoretical physicists were beginning to invoke conceptual models for the energy states and electronic properties of solids. In 1928 Sommerfeld developed a better understanding of conduction in metals, and in 1931 Wilson published his famous work which established the energy-band model and the role of valence, conduction and forbidden energy bands. These advances, of course, were very much based on the new concepts of quantum theory, statistical mechanics, and the Schrödinger equation, which had been introduced in the 1920's and were now finding a wide range of applications in the physical world.

Based on the Wilson model of semiconductors, a number of their body properties became more readily understood, such as the temperature dependence of conductivity, conduction and photoconduction, and in the late 1930's the roles of donor and acceptor impurities, electrons and positive holes, and the chemical picture (based on bonding) of electrons being ionized from bands into the freely conducting state. A conceptual blind-spot that persisted for some years was an awareness of the important role of minority carriers. Progress was less rapid with the surface properties. Good rectifiers seemed more an art than a science. Experimentally, correlation was established between the direction and rectification and the sign of the majority carrier of the semiconductor, but early theories (by Mott, Schottky, Davidoff) predicted the wrong direction of rectification. It turned out later this was because the role of minority carriers was overlooked.

As research into the properties of semiconductors progressed, it was realized more and more how vital was the ability to control the composition and structure of the materials. Chemists and metallurgists were appealed to for help in getting purer silicon and later (after recognizing how n- or p-type, rectification direction, and accidental p–n junctions correlated with impurity segregation) for controlling amounts of identified impurities which in turn led to control over the n- or p-type nature of a semiconductor. Such was the state-of-the-art when World War II struck. Based on this art, nevertheless, many important semiconductor devices were produced, notably for microwave detectors in radar.

When the War ended, following Kelly's urging outlined earlier, researchers at Bell Laboratories resumed the attack on semiconductors. They had the intuitive feeling that, if only they understood semiconductors better and had more control over the material, important new electronic devices, particularly amplifiers, would be forthcoming. Specifically, Shockley believed that it should be possible to modulate the resistance of a thin layer of semiconductor by imposing a strong electric-field gradient across the layer, and then quickly and controllably changing the number of available carriers of current. It was obvious that electronic amplification could be based on this effect if it existed. Thus, several physicists, chemists, metallurgists and electrical engineers started working together in the interdisciplinary MSE mode. The years 1945 - 1948 saw much experimentation, the posing of phenomenological models, the failure to confirm the model with experiment, the devising of new models, predictions of certain effects which experiment failed to confirm, and so on — a familiar scenario to researchers striving towards a deep understanding of nature. New concepts had to be proposed to replace the old ones that had failed. An important advance was Bardeen's theory of surface states, which was introduced in order to explain the failure to observe the large field effects in solid-state triode structures that Shockley had expected. This idea led to a realization of the importance of minority carriers in the behavior of contacts. And in 1948, the point contact transistor was discovered by Bardeen and Brattain. It is clear that these unanticipated, important and radically new results emerged from the steady pursuit of exact science with a purposeful goal, and not simply from the elaboration of known technology.

Once the role of minority carriers had been understood, Shockley quickly followed with the prediction of the junction transistor, both p–n–p and n–p–n. The potential performance of such junction devices appeared more promising than that of the point-contact transistor, particularly for its stability and its power-handling capacity. But to realize such a structure called for even better control over material preparation. From this point on, it is perhaps fair to say that, though physicists and electrical engineers continued to have many of the device ideas, the pace of progress in semiconductor research and development was determined very much by the progress of the chemists and metallurgists. Absolutely vital steps were the discovery of zone-refining by Pfann and the development of ways to grow high quality single crystals of germanium and silicon. As a result, the grown junction transistor was demonstrated in 1951.

New methods of preparing junctions and transistors with improved performance followed quickly: first alloying, then diffusion processes. New devices and applications were not far behind, including silicon power rectifiers and solar "batteries". The family of useful semiconductors was extended in 1953 by Welker working at Siemens in Germany, who showed that a range of binary compounds based on the Group III and Group V columns of the periodic table were analogs of the Group IV elements, silicon and germanium. These new compounds were eventually to lead to whole new classes of important semiconductor devices.

The materials work, directed towards improving the technology of semiconductor devices, proved a rich source of new fundamental understanding of materials. Important spin-offs were better control over doping, the identification of impurities, new techniques for growing crystals, deeper understanding of solid-state solution theory and crystal-growth kinetics, thermodynamic theory and, by no means least, the nature and consequences of dislocations. The last topic, for which solid-state research laid much of the groundwork, was to have far-reaching influences in other areas of MSE.

And so solid-state electronics was born.

Development of Coated Stainless Steel Razor Blades*

In an industry which might be thought of as experience-based, the internal objective to achieve substantial improvement in shaving performance led to a materials research and development program requiring considerable science and sophisticated techniques.

In the decade beginning with the year 1945, an interdisciplinary group of scientists and engineers at the Gillette Company began a long-range study of the properties and uses of razors and razor blades. This group comprised chemists (polymer, organic and physical), metallurgists and physicists as well as me-

---

*This account was furnished by I. W. Fischbein, Gillette R & D Laboratory.

chanical and electronic engineers. The use of a then new scientific diagnostic instrument, the scanning electron microscope, provided for the first time a way of measuring the performance difference of various razor-blade materials. A key point in the program was the somewhat accidental observation of deposition of thin films of polymers on steel surfaces. The major feature, however, was the organizational climate and the ability of the investigators to recognize the importance of this observation and to exploit it properly for their overall objective. Materials research and development seldom runs a neatly planned course; it requires perception, training and freedom to capitalize on an unexpected event or observation. The result was a new, hard-alloy coating of the blade, covered, in turn, by a thin, tough plastic layer.

After considerable difficulty, techniques were devised to study razor-blade edges with the electron microscope. This new tool showed that the heretofore unresolved edge dimension was a few hundred ångström units on mass-produced razor blades. For the first time, it was possible to demonstrate that the mechanism of failure in service was different for high carbon steel blades than for stainless steel blades. These studies also showed that the carbon steel blades were being chemically eroded during shaving. This led to a program to reduce the deterioration of carbon steel edges during shaving. One of the means explored to accomplish this end was to coat the carbon-steel edges with metal coatings. Most of these were applied by vacuum evaporation of the metal onto the edges. Because of the very small ultimate edge dimension of the blade, these coatings were kept very thin, no more than a few hundred ångströms at the most. Improved shaving life of carbon steel blades resulted with some sacrifice in initial shaving quality.

While this work was proceeding, one of those side experiments, so common in research, was performed. This experiment was to test whether a high molecular weight polymer could be transferred across a vacuum onto a metal surface to form a continuous coating. Polytetrafluoroethylene (PTFE) was chosen as the polymer for the test because of its extremely high heat stability. The transfer was conducted onto razor blade edges (rather than on the articles then of primary interest) solely because razor blades were the most convenient objects available to be used in the particular apparatus employed. The PTFE was heated in an incandescent tungsten coil until an increase in pressure in the vacuum chamber was observed. The razor-blade edges were examined after deposition by light microscopy. Wetting tests showed that some PTFE had indeed transferred across the vacuum chamber. Further tests showed that, contrary to expectations, the cutting ability of razor blades had been improved by the PTFE coating. Subsequent shaving with these blades showed an improvement beyond that normally obtainable with uncoated blades.

This was the first time a razor blade had been obtained with a shaving quality above and beyond that obtainable by normal sharpening practice and despite the fact that a rather thick coating had been bonded to the ultimate edge of the sharpened blade.

This discovery led, in due course, to an exhaustive study of fluorocarbons for coating razor-blade edges. It was clear from the initial experiment that degradation of the high molecular weight PTFE had taken place and that a lower molecular weight material had actually been deposited onto the blade edges. Studies of the "evaporated PTFE" showed it to have a lower melting point and higher crystallinity than the starting material.

Attempts were made by the group to synthesize fluorocarbons of carefully controlled molecular weights. Great difficulty was encountered in this work and soon help was sought outside the company from a large chemical manufacturer expert in this field. A major problem with commercially available high molecular weight PTFE was the particle size combined with the very high melt viscosity. These polymer particles failed to flow and coalesce into a pore-free film when heated well above their melting point. Although the particles did sinter to form an adherent bonded film on the blade edge, adequate surface coverage required several layers of particles in the film. Since virtually no flow of the particles took place during sintering, the resulting PTFE film thickness was of the order of a micron or more. This film thickness was detrimental to initial shaving quality and as a result, a "break-in" period of several shaves was required as the film wore thinner before optimum shaving quality could be realized.

To avoid this loss of initial shaving quality, a PTFE-type polymer with a melt viscosity in which the melted particles would flow freely and coalesce during sintering was sought. PTFE-type polymers and telomers with molecular weights ranging from as low as a thousand to as high as several million were made. The very low-molecular weight PTFE, while flowing freely, failed with respect to shaving life of the film on blades. Intermediate molecular weight material from about 30 000 to 200 000 exhibited the desired melt-flow properties for film formation and, surprisingly, produced blades of shaving life exceeding that of the very high molecular weight commercial PTFE polymers. PTFE-type polymers in this molecular weight range could produce much thinner pore-free films (of the order of 0.1 - 0.2 μm) which showed excellent shaving quality from the very first shave.

The improved flow properties of these polymers led to easier film-thickness control in mass production.

Concurrently with the work on synthesizing new fluorocarbon polymers, studies were made of high molecular-weight PTFE and its behavior when heated on different metallic surfaces in a variety of gases. This work showed that there was an interaction between the PTFE, the metal and the gas to produce a variety of different PTFE coatings under the same heating conditions.

Studies of PTFE-coated blades were made after various stages of shaving. It was possible to show that the PTFE coating persisted around the ultimate edge of the blade for several shaves. The PTFE coatings were removed from the blade edge after shaving by dissolving the steel and floating off the coating, which could be shown to remain intact across the ultimate edge in many places.

More recent work on razor blades, where electron microscopy and physical metallurgy have played a predominant role, has been the development of edge-strengthening metallic alloy coatings. Studies of evaporated and sputtered metallic coatings for razor-blade edges have led to the use of an ordered alloy of platinum and chromium. This alloy, with a super-lattice of the intermetallic compound Cr_3Pt, when coated on razor-blade edges and then overcoated with PTFE, provides blades edges of excellent shaving life. While it is easy to demonstrate the presence of the ordered superlattice structure of the Cr_3Pt alloy in bulk melted samples by conventional X-ray diffraction techniques, it is extremely difficult to show this in thin films on razor-blade edges. However, a careful electron microscope and electron diffraction analysis of alloy coatings, 300 - 500 Å thin, reveals that an inter-metallic compound with the characteristic A15 cubic ordered crystal structure does form in these vapor-deposited thin films. The grain size was shown to be extremely small and the presence of some lattice defects was found within the fine grains. It was not possible to analyze the structure by any other technique. Under some circumstances, the line broadening due to small grain size and lattice defects was so great that the characteristic lines effectively overlapped, giving rise to a broad diffuse ring in the electron diffraction pattern.

The Cr_3Pt alloy exhibits a DPHN hardness in excess of 1400. This is far above the normal hardness of PTFE-coated razor blades which range in hardness from 550 to 650 DPHN. X-ray diffraction techniques have made it possible to characterize the structure of the Cr_3Pt alloy in bulk, while the electron microscope has made similar analysis possible in thin films useful for razor-blade edges.

Synthetic Fibers*

Textile materials have been developed over many hundreds of years and the most suitable natural fibers have provided the basis for today's textile industry. These natural (as opposed to synthetic) textile fibers are cotton, wool, flax and silk, with silk giving the highest strength properties. Except that silk is spun by the silkworm, methods for the spinning and weaving of natural fibers have been accepted routines since before the Industrial Revolution,

Although still of great importance, natural fibers have given way to the science and engineering developments of regenerated (natural) fibers and more significantly to the developments of synthetic fibers. Synthetic fibers are those in which man has chemically synthesized the fiber-forming polymer-base material and engineered the operation of fiber production through the use of machines, in contrast to relying on either plant or animal life to do either of these jobs.

The development of the synthetic fiber industry as we know it today required intense interfacing of various MSE disciplines. An excellent example of this

is the story of "nylon", a duPont polyamide fiber. Nylon emerged as a very important lightweight, high-strength fiber during World War II for making parachutes, rope, tire cord, etc., and subsequently for producing hosiery and other important textile materials. As is the case for other synthetic fibers, the fiber is spun from a polymer-base material synthesized from basic chemicals derived from coal, oil, etc. (materials science). Nylon fiber is obtained from the polymer-base material by melting it and squeezing it through tiny holes (spinning) into thin strands which are stretched like taffy into the filaments desired (materials engineering).

The way for the convergence of MSE to produce nylon was paved by the starting of a "pure research" program in 1928 aimed to obtain fundamental knowledge. DuPont history tells us that the initial purpose of the program was for future company diversification, but not oriented toward a specific product. It should be recognized, however, that the selection of Dr. Wallace H. Carothers (1896 - 1937) from the Harvard faculty, who was known to have intense interests in the field of polymer chemistry, to head up this research program is an indication that the future importance of synthetic polymer science and engineering was foreseen.

The advancing materials science provided the capabilities for synthesizing the new high molecular weight polymers required, and engineering disciplines provided the know-how for causing the macromolecular chains of these materials to align under the shear of extrusion through spinnerets. It was also learned that after extrusion the spun fiber could be further stretched to improve the molecular alignment of chains for enhanced strength and performance characteristics. To reach the ultimate customer, this materials advance also required innovations in spinning and weaving machinery for the new fibers.

Born in the 20th century, polymer science is one of today's most important materials sciences. A polymer molecule is a giant molecule made up of many thousands or millions of simple molecules linked together into long chain-like structures (macromolecules). All natural fibers are made up of macromolecules, and the important mechanical properties of fibers are the result of interactions between the long chains. Long-chain molecules are lined up parallel to each other in fiber formation. The better this alignment is, the stronger are the interactions between polymer chains, and the higher is the tensile strength of the fiber.

In the late 1920's, there was an awareness of the importance of polymeric materials. Natural materials were known to be made of giant molecules or polymers and in particular the value of polymer materials such as wool, cotton and man-made rayon was known. Also, early ground work in the field of polymer synthesis was being laid in a few laboratories, but no work had been successful at that time in synthesizing a polymer which could be made into a synthetic fiber with useful properties.

Observations of the silkworm making its cocoon provided important inputs to early efforts to produce unnatural fibers. The silkworm had long afforded clues for the development of engineering processes

---

*Alan Lovelace of the U. S. National Aeronautics and Space Administration provided this account.

for producing synthetic fibers since it was known to extrude a liquid substance through its glands, solidifying into a continuous filament on emerging into cool air. The engineer could simulate this by forcing a substance (either in solution or melted) through a spinneret with small orifices and achieve much the same results, provided that the substance being spun would hang together and subsequently withstand high stresses or pulling. Polymeric substances (long-chain molecules) should be capable of this.

Spinning polymeric materials from solution was being investigated before the 1920's in developing the basic art for producing rayon fibers. Chemically degrading high polymeric natural cellulose by either acid (acetate process) or alkali (viscose process) to a somewhat lower molecular weight derivative, and then subsequently regenerating the cellulosic material from solution in the form of fibers had been accomplished. The lowered molecular weight of the regenerated cellulose fibers rendered them weaker than silk fibers which possessed their high natural molecular weight, and so the high-strength problem for synthetic fibers had not been solved.

A large body of knowledge had been amassed and engineering aspects on the spinning and the packaging of rayon for market had been worked out by the time Carothers' group became productive in the preparation of new synthetic polymers. The possible impact of synthetic fibers on the textile industry and society was realized to some extent. The knowledge that linear synthetic polymers of very high molecular weight ("superpolymers") could give rise to high strength fibers to replace silk for many important applications was already in the minds of astute engineers and scientists. About 1935 the decision to commercialize nylon was made, and the development problems were handed to the engineers producing rayon (man-made fiber from natural polymer-cellulose).

When Carothers was brought in by duPont, he chose to investigate polymerization by condensation as well as the structure of high molecular weight substances. About a dozen chemists worked under his personal supervision, principally organic and physical chemists, the former to synthesize polymers and the latter to determine their properties.

The role of the research chemists and their discoveries cannot be overemphasized in discussing the origins of synthetic fibers. By synthesizing new polymeric materials unknown in nature, by recognizing their importance, and by synthesizing them in molecular weights high enough to be useful (in this case, for being converted to fibers with strengths to compete with silk), the organic chemists achieved great successes.

The chemical research led to synthetic procedures for polyamides, polyesters, polyanhydrides, and neoprene rubber — all synthetic polymers. The early research on polyesters opened the way to many important scientific observations. It was found that molten polymers could be drawn out into threads using a glass rod. It was further found that these threads could be pulled (cold drawn) to several times the original length of the thread and that the resulting drawn filament would exhibit much higher tensile strength than the undrawn filament. However, the drawn fiber still had the ability to undergo elongation under stress, an important fiber property.

Another significant discovery of the research team was the fact that the drawn fiber polyester appeared to be nearly as strong when wet as it was when dry. This was very definitely an improvement over natural man-made cellulosic fibers or yarn. When investigated by X-ray diffraction, the polyester fiber showed an orientation of crystalline phase similar to that of silk and rayon fiber. It was later observed that polyester could be dry spun from chloroform-like acetate rayon, and it could also be cold drawn.

The research group of synthetic chemists was able to prepare linear polyesters having molecular weights above 10 000 (superpolymers) which were fiber forming. However, because of their low melting points, their lack of stability and their solubilities in a number of solvents, the polyesters did not show promise as textile fibers at that time. The useful properties of polyesters for fibers were not recognized until additional key concepts and properties associated with aromatic polyesters were discovered by J. R. Whinfield and J. T. Dickson at the end of the 1930's.

Without the benefit of future knowledge about aromatic polyesters, the Carothers group concentrated its research on the polyamides synthesized in the early 30's. The synthetic polymer which was chosen for fiber development was that synthesized from hexamethylenediamine and adipic acid in the mid 30's. Each one of these monomers contains a small six-carbon chain and so the polyamide synthesized from these monomers was referred to as a 66 polymer, later called Nylon 66. This was the synthetic polymer to which engineers with fifteen or so years' experience in the rayon textile field devoted their attention as the development of nylon was commenced. The basic principles of the synthesis and the needs for high molecular weights and fiber orientation were established.

Although the research in chemistry did not cease, it was now the time for the engineers (and engineering science) to be called upon. Much experience and technical skill had been acquired in the production of rayon, and these people had valuable experience in spinning, weaving and knitting of rayon. Despite the depth of experience in the engineering science of textiles, new innovations and discoveries were required to solve the problems specifically associated with the spinning and weaving of this purely synthetic fiber. The problems in processing and equipment design were immense.

Before a satisfactory solution to the spinning of nylon was arrived at, an entirely new concept of melt spinning at temperatures approaching 300 °C was derived. Instead of extruding a solution of polymer into a coagulation bath where fibers are hardened by precipitation (wet spinning) or into a hot gas chamber where fibers are hardened by evaporation of the solvent (dry spinning), the nylon polymer was heated above its melting point of 263 °C and the molten polymer extruded into a cool gas chamber for hardening the fiber (melt spinning).

Developing a pumping system with the required small clearances for the hot molten polymer, and the use of the polymer itself as a lubricant, constituted an engineering accomplishment in itself. Special non-softening, non-warping, abrasion-resistant steels had to be utilized. Problems involved with properties of polymers could not be handled by classical fluid mechanics based on small-molecule behavior. The engineers were required to confront new design problems to produce new textile equipment since the rayon and acetate equipment was not adaptable to this new synthetic polymer. Nevertheless, they were successful in commencing pilot production of nylon in 1938.

In addition to the contributions of the organic and physical chemists, one might further distinguish a contributing discipline by reference to analytical chemistry. For example, the chemists synthesizing the new polymers were aided greatly by the wet chemical analysis performed by analytical chemists to determine the number of chain ends which were still present in a polymerization mixture. By detecting the number of chain ends in a sample, the analytical chemist could calculate the number of molecules which had linked together to tell him the molecular weight which had been achieved. Analysis and determination of molecular weights of giant molecules was in its infancy around 1930. The development of this analytical capability for polymers gave the organic chemist necessary information from which he could develop reaction conditions to increase and control the molecular weights obtained from the polymerization reactions. As indicated above, high molecular weight "superpolymers" were required in order to obtain fibers with tensile strengths comparable to that obtained from silk.

During the early days of research on the polyesters and polyamides, another materials science played an important role in the development of synthetic fibers. That materials science was physics. Physicists had previously investigated natural and regenerated natural fibers by X-ray diffraction methods. Diffraction patterns indicating orientation of the long polymer-chain molecules in silk were understood to a large extent, and the effects of drawing to orient polymer chains and improve strength in rayon fibers were known. The physicist then developed structure-property relationships of great fundamental importance and contributed greatly to the understanding of the high tensile strength obtained from cold drawing the early filaments produced by the organic chemists. The knowledge of polymer orientation from X-ray diffraction was directly applied to the synthetic fiber research.

Prior developments in the field of metallurgy, as a part of MSE, had to be relied upon by the engineers who dealt with the problems of spinning nylon. When the time came to scale up the polymerization reactions of nylon, the engineers used copper vessels in initial runs. However, when molten polymer was extruded from the copper vessels, it was found to be dark in color indicating that a chemical reaction had taken place between the metal vessels and the molten polymer at temperatures approaching 300 °C. A search

had to be made for different types of materials which were more corrosion-resistant in the large scale environment. Glass vessels were known to be acceptable because these had been used previously in the laboratory. But of all the other materials tested in an extensive search, only silver and stainless steel were found to resist corrosion when in contact with the molten nylon polymerization mixture. Although the technology of stainless steel was still in relatively early stages of development, it was fortunate that significant developments had been made in this area of MSE to be able to furnish a quality of stainless steel which could be utilized under the high temperature conditions imposed by the new melt-spinning method.

Textured Materials*

Textured materials is a description used here to refer to polycrystalline microstructures in which a degree of control is exercised on the alignment of neighboring crystals. Examples are permanent magnet alloys, and high strength phosphor bronze alloys for use as springs in relays and connectors.

The central theme of materials science in the relation between composition, structure and properties is beautifully illustrated by this research program in a loose coupling mode. Basic work by a physicist, followed many years later by metallurgical research and by extensive computational techniques from the mathematicians, has led to a capability for predicting the structure and related physical properties of materials in terms of the processing steps used in the preparation. This program has set a high standard for the direct contributions which MSE can make to practical programs.

Most materials in use today are polycrystalline aggregates of a large number of microscopic crystals, or grains. The directional alignment among neighboring crystals ranges from random to nearly perfect. We call a material textured when a reasonably good alignment occurs. Thus, a textured material resembles somewhat a giant crystal. Because a crystal may be mechanically stronger or more magnetic in one direction than another, properties of polycrystalline materials can be enhanced by texturing.

Texture is developed in several ways. One method starts with cast ingots. When an ingot is deformed, such as by rolling or wire drawing, textural changes take place. Interestingly enough, the crystals often do not assume random orientations when the deformed material is subsequently annealed. A new set of crystals forms by recrystallization and the new crystals often take on a new texture with a different orientation from the old texture.

The basic mathematics of analyzing the development of texture during deformation was worked out by the mathematical physicist, Sir Geoffrey I. Taylor, in Cambridge in 1937. The treatment is essentially one of optimization, calling for the selection of a set of slip planes and directions that would accomplish the deformation with a minimum expenditure of

---

*Contributions to this account were provided by G. Y. Chin of Bell Telephone Laboratories.

mechanical work. Widespread application of the analysis, however, was delayed because of the extremely laborious calculations involved at the time. With the development of linear programming in the 1940's and with the advent of electronic computers, successful application of Taylor's treatment became assured. This was done in a collaborative effort between a research metallurgist and a mathematician who have been able to trace the texture development by modeling the deformation on a computer. Graphic computer plots are generated which not only reveal the final texture of the crystals within the polycrystalline material, but how it is arrived at as well. Thus, a considerable degree of textural control can be exercised.

Recent studies have led to advances in understanding how texture is developed — an essential first step in the control and exploitation of this phenomenon in materials.

In one study, undertaken by two research metallurgists, the formation of texture in castings was simulated and followed by observing the steps by which freezing occurs in certain transparent, nonmetallic materials that possess thermodynamic properties similar to those of metals. The study of castings of these transparent materials has led to better understanding and control of texture in castings. An impressive application of texture control by casting is in the use of directional solidification for turbine blades for jet engines. Other metallurgists concerned with finding improved magnetic alloys have also employed directional solidification to enhance the magnetic properties of powerful permanent magnet alloys made of cobalt, copper and samarium (or cerium). Commercial Alnico permanent magnets have likewise been improved by texture control via directional solidification. This type of texture control is particularly suitable for brittle materials which cannot be mechanically deformed.

If the material is ductile, deformation processes such as wire drawing and rolling can also produce texture. During deformation, certain crystal planes glide over each other, forcing the individual crystals to assume a common directional alignment. These crystal planes can vary from one material to another, thereby producing different textures.

The degree of control over the crystal texture is primarily a function of how the material is deformed. By adjusting die sizes, or the roll spacing through which the metal is passed, the metal is reduced in successive stages. Depending on the sequence and extent of reduction, different textures can be obtained and, therefore, different physical and mechanical properties from the metal. Within the Bell System, such control has led to improved soft magnetic alloys in wire and tape form for use in certain magnetic memory devices and also to alloys with enhanced mechanical properties for springs and electrical connectors. In the latter, after final heat treatment, yield strengths of such materials as phosphor bronze, nickel silver, cupronickel and copper beryllium have been, on the average, almost doubled without loss of ductility.

Elsewhere, texture strengthening has been responsible for increased strength in spherical pressure vessels of titanium alloys. In one example, a pressure vessel made of textured Ti–5%Al–2.5%Sn alloy sheet exhibited a yield strength level 40 per cent higher than that predicted for randomly oriented material, and the burst strength was about 75 per cent higher than that available without texture control. Improved mechanical properties in magnesium and beryllium have also been attained through texture control.

Texture control has been and continues to be a major activity aiming to upgrade the quality of deep-drawing sheet steels. These steels are consumed in huge quantities as automobile body fenders and appliance housings, to name two of their numberous uses. How deep a cup can be drawn from a blank depends heavily on the strength of the cup wall and on the ease of deformation in the flange region. It has been theoretically predicted, and experimentally proven, that improved drawability can be achieved given the proper texture. In addition, "ears", or undulations of the rim, which must be trimmed away, are directly related to the texture and can be suppressed through texture control. Textured deep-drawing steels are now offered on a limited commercial basis.

These studies emphasize the positive aspects of textured materials. Occasions do arise, however, when texture may be undesirable. For example, some recent work has indicated that thin-film capacitors made from textured films of aluminium or hafnium perform poorly compared with those made from randomly oriented materials. Hence, texture control implies suppression as well as accentuation of texture.

Integrated Circuits*

Although this is a logical follow-on to the transistor story, integrated circuits are included as a separate piece because other aspects of MSE are illustrated. In the rapid development of integrated circuits, effective coupling was achieved principally through cross-licensing of patents among competitive industrial organizations.

Whereas the transistor required important new scientific understanding, the creation of the sophisticated integrated circuits resulted principally from inventiveness and engineering ingenuity, particularly in processing technology. At the same time, the small dimensions and extreme material purity needed for integrated circuits could not be achieved without a wide array of diagnostic tools and instrumentation provided by earlier unrelated scientific programs.

The development of the transistor had led to a number of basic techniques required for integrated circuits, such as semiconductor purification, crystal growth, alloying, diffusion, oxide masking and epitaxial growth. The semiconductor industry had reached the point in 1958, when the integrated circuit was born, where it worked daily with crystals of chemical, physical and structural perfection many orders of magnitude higher than in any other industry and produced novel, discrete, electronic devices, often with superior performance to that of vacuum tubes.

---

*This account was furnished by Morton Jones of Texas Instruments, Inc.

Silicon was beginning to become important, though germanium was the predominant semiconductor material. Silicon looked particularly promising in military applications where its superior high temperature performance was necessary. Transistors were being designed into circuits for which small size and weight and low power drain were critical, though the cost was still not competitive with vacuum tubes. The first commercial products to use significant quantities of transistors were miniature hearing aids and portable radios. Computers and communications were obvious candidates in the industrial area, and IBM and Bell Laboratories had large semiconductor programs. Another was the development of military equipment such as the Polaris and Minuteman missile programs. All of these large-system applications of semiconductor devices spurred the push to miniaturization. This then was the status of semiconductors in 1958 when Kilby at Texas Instruments Inc. first conceived of and constructed an integrated circuit. Though the practical use of transistors was relatively new, the needs for even further reduction in size, weight and power were already in sight.

Kilby, an electrical engineer, joined Texas Instruments from Centralab Electronics where he had been working on miniaturization of electronic circuits by the silk screening of conductive inks on a ceramic substrate to form resistance and capacitance. Hence, he had experience and a strong interest in miniaturization. In 1958, he conceived of processing the elements of a complete circuit, such as resistors, capacitors and diodes in a monolithic bar of semiconductor. The technology for accomplishing this already existed, having been developed for fabricating discrete devices. Diffusion and alloying were used for introducing controlled amounts of desired impurities to create localized p and n regions. Metal evaporation and thermocompression bonding were available for making electrical contacts to and between such regions. Kilby's first working semiconductor circuit was a simple phase-shift oscillator with components connected either through the bulk semiconductor when resistance was desired, or by bonding wires between them. This technology permitted fabrication of only simple circuits involving a few tens of devices, and several subsequent advances were necessary before the complex, reliable and inexpensive integrated circuits of today became a reality. Some of the more important of these advances were made in the continuing effort to improve discrete transistors as mentioned earlier; however, their application to integrated circuits was rapidly recognized and exploited.

The key developments were (a) the application of photoresist and oxide etches to determine the regions into which impurities were to be diffused, (b) the planar process using the above techniques for diffusion but leaving the silicon oxide layer on the surface to protect the ambient-sensitive p–n junctions, (c) the use of evaporated and photoresist-patterned metal films on the oxide to interconnect the devices, and (d) the application of chemical vapor deposition for growing thin epitaxial layers of silicon on silicon substrates containing different impurity doping. Each of these developments, and their application to integrated circuit improvement, will be briefly described.

The ability of an SiO_2 layer to mask against the diffusion of many of the group III and V doping impurities was described by Frosch, a chemist at Bell Laboratories, in 1957. A wax pattern was applied to the oxide, the unprotected regions chemically etched away to expose the silicon, the wax removed, and impurities diffused into the exposed regions to form p- and n-doped material. Though this technique was useful, it was limited to formation of relatively large regions, several hundred microns in size. Photosensitive materials, known as photoresists, had been developed at Eastman Kodak for the patterned etching of metal on printing plates and on printed circuit boards. These were solutions containing organic compounds which polymerized upon exposure to ultraviolet light. The unexposed resist could be dissolved by appropriate solvents leaving an etch-resistant mask on the metal. Lathrop, a physicist, and Nall, a chemist, working on miniaturization of components at Diamond Ordnance Fuse Laboratory, realized in 1957 that photoresist might be applicable to patterning the SiO_2 for silicon-diffused transistors. This allowed windows of the order of 200 μm in size to be etched. Continued improvements in photoresists, with emphasis on their use with semiconductors, increased their definition capabilities to about 25 μm by 1960 and to less than 1 μm today. A major advantage in these photoresist techniques is the ability to pattern all of the areas on a 2 in diameter silicon slice simultaneously, with consequent reduction in processing cost.

The next major technological advance was the planar process, developed by Hoerni, a physicist at Fairchild Semiconductor Division. This process applies the oxide-masking and photoresist technologies already described; however, SiO_2 is regrown into the windows during the diffusion steps and the oxide is left over all of the device or circuit surface except the contact areas. This has two major advantages. The oxide, as had been shown by Atalla at Bell Laboratories, eliminates slow surface states and protects the sensitive regions (where p–n junctions intercept the silicon surface) from the effect of ambients, thereby leading to improved device characteristics and greater reliability. Also the oxide is a good insulator and allows evaporated metallization patterns connecting the devices to be formed directly on the oxide surface. Again, photoresist techniques are used to define these metal interconnections patterns. It is also possible, by depositing another SiO_2 layer over the first metallization, to form a second set of interconnections allowing even more complex circuits to be fabricated.

Still another significant development necessary for the success of integrated circuits was the application of chemical vapor deposition to grow epitaxial silicon layers. Circuits made with planar technology, but on bulk silicon slices, had severe limitations. Many circuits required significantly better electrical isolation between individual regions or devices than was afforded by the bulk silicon resistance alone. Hence, such circuits could not be integrated. Epitaxial growth, as will be described, allowed suitable isolation to be achieved.

Chemical vapor deposition for growing single crystals of silicon and germanium was demonstrated in the early 1950's by Sangster, a chemist at Hughes Aircraft Company, and by Teal and Christensen, chemists at Bell Laboratories. The conductivity type and resistivity of the deposited semiconductors could be controlled by introducing appropriate impurity gases during the deposition. Several investigators attempted to use this technique for growing successive multiple n- and p-type layers to form diodes and transistors directly, rather than by starting with uniform material and altering regions by impurity diffusion. However, these attempts gave poor results. The characteristics of the resulting p-n junctions were poor, probably due to imperfections or contamination at the interfaces between the layers. Whereas diffusion could be patterned into localized areas, there was no comparable way of patterning the epitaxial regions. However, an interdisciplinary team at Bell Laboratories, Loar (physicist), Christensen (chemist), Kleimack (physicist) and Theurer (metallurgist), realized and demonstrated that a more limited use of epitaxial deposition could significantly improve planar transistor performance.

The diffused base and emitter regions in planar transistors are quite shallow, extending only a few, or at most a few tens, of microns in from the silicon surface. Yet, in order to be handled during processing without excessive breakage, the silicon slices must be several times that thickness. Since the resistivity in the collector region adjacent to the base needs to be of the order of 1 Ω cm, the extra thickness adds additional collector series resistance which is detrimental to transistor performance. By starting with a heavily doped, hence low resistivity, silicon slice of sufficient thickness to provide the necessary mechanical strength, and growing a lightly doped epitaxial layer only thick enough to contain the active regions of the transistor, a significant reduction was obtained in collector series resistance.

This same technique was subsequently applied to silicon integrated circuits to achieve electrical isolation between components. A thin n-type epitaxial layer suitable for fabrication of the desired devices was grown on a p-type silicon substrate. During processing, a group III impurity was diffused through the thin n-layer to the p-type substrate in a pattern that surrounded those devices requiring isolation with p-type material. The high resistance of the reversed bias p-n junction provided the isolation.

Based on the technologies which have been described, integrated circuits containing bipolar transistors as the active devices were developed to perform a variety of electronic functions and a major commercial business resulted. Meanwhile, back in the laboratories, a new active semiconductor device was being studied, the metal-oxide-semiconductor (MOS) transistor. It is interesting to note that the MOS transistor is in essence the field-effect device that Shockley had originally sought, but only more recently made possible through advances in materials technology. This device had significant advantages over bipolar transistors for some applications. The electrical power requirements were lower. High packing densities on integrated circuits were possible and fewer processing operations were required during manufacturing, resulting in higher yields and lower costs. However, the device also brought new technical problems which had to be solved before its usefulness could be realized.

Inasmuch as the critical, active region of the MOS transistor lies very close to the silicon-SiO_2 interface, the instabilities in the SiO_2 and near the interface strongly influence the transistor properties. Such instabilities can be caused by many things, a common one being the presence of sodium ion contamination in the SiO_2. The high electronic field present across the oxide during operation of the device causes the sodium to migrate, and transistor characteristics shift accordingly. Many man-years of effort in several laboratories by chemists, physicists and electrical engineers were required before the causes of, and cures for, these instabilities reached a point where reliable MOS integrated circuits became practical. This area is now growing rapidly in importance, with integrated circuits containing as many as 10 000 individual components being manufactured in high volume and incorporated into equipment such as electronic desk and hand calculators.

So the integrated circuit has evolved, in a little over a decade, from Kilby's first phase-shift oscillator with a few components to the large-scale manufacturing of circuits with over 10 000 components, and these at much lower cost and higher reliability than the sum of the individual components.

The critical steps in the integrated-circuit story are shown in Fig. 1. The overall effort was both multidisciplinary and interdisciplinary. Chemists and metallurgists developed epitaxial growth techniques with the scope of the studies ranging from basic investigations of the kinetics and thermodynamics of the vapor-solid reactions to the design of production reactors capable of handling several slices at a time. A chemist discovered the diffusion-masking ability of SiO_2. A physicist, who had previously spent several years in a university chemistry department, conceived of the planar process. A physicist and chemist first applied photoresist methods to semiconductors. Metallurgists perfected the metal systems evaporated onto the surface for interconnecting the components. Electrical engineers designed the devices and circuits, and laid out the diffusion-masking and interconnection patterns so that circuits would perform the desired functions. Today, because of the extreme complexity of circuits containing in excess of 10 000 components, layout and interconnection patterns are performed on computers, requiring programmers and software specialists, and they must interact closely with the chemists, physicists and process engineers to ensure compatibility between the design and the process capabilities. Finally, metallurgists and ceramic engineers developed the hermetically sealed packages to protect the silicon circuits.

Interaction between science and engineering certainly existed to a high degree. While investigators were busy writing up their work for publication in scientific journals, they were simultaneously phasing their developments into the production lines. The time between scientific advance and production was extremely short.

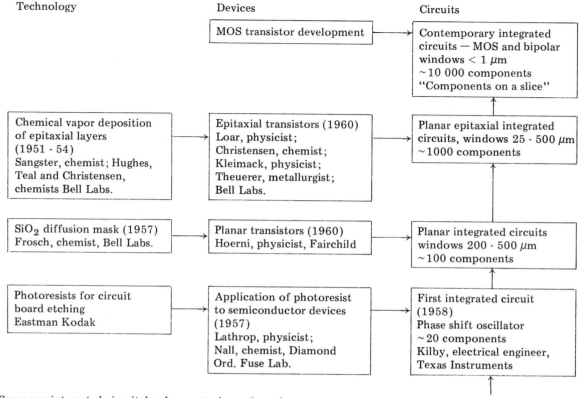

Fig. 1. Key integrated-circuit developments, 1958-1971.

The technological advances described here borrowed very heavily from developments in other areas. Nearly all were motivated by attempts to improve the performance of discrete transistors rather than integrated circuits. Diffusion of impurities had been studied for years in other materials, such as metals. Photoresist was developed for the printing and circuit-board industries. But those concerned with the perfection of the integrated circuit quickly recognized the applicability of such techniques.

There were certainly many individuals and institutions involved, both in the initial discoveries and even more in the subsequent development into useful processes. Few of the significant contributions to process technology involved basic research. Most grew out of applied research and engineering, with the latter predominating.

The development of integrated circuits, in fact the entire development of modern electronic devices, was not only a case where the MSE approach was followed, but one where this approach was essential for success to be achieved so effectively.

Aluminum Conductors*

Copper conductors for electricity come from an experience-based industry, but problems in copper availability have injected new science and engineering into the technology. Although aluminum as it existed a few years ago was unsatisfactory for many copper–wire applications, materials research and development has demonstrated that it is possible to modify and control aluminum alloys to meet the necessary properties, such as electrical conductivity, ductility and corrosion resistance. The objectives of the program were clear, the time scale was relatively short and the

---

*Contributions to this account were provided by T. D. Schlabach of Bell Telephone Laboratories.

contributions were more of an engineering nature than scientific. This is a clear example of the user in a science-intensive industry demanding new material capabilities and providing leadership to attain that end. It illustrates the ability to develop, through materials research and development, a substitute material to satisfy a specified function.

In 1965 the Bell System undertook an extensive development project with the specific aim of establishing an aluminum-conductor telephone-cable technology as a commercially viable alternative to copper conductor cable. The major impetus for this development, as with most other substitutions of aluminum for copper in electrical applications, stemmed from periodic instabilities in both the price and availability of copper. As the largest single consumer of copper in the U. S. (approximately 250 000 tons or 12 per cent of all the copper used in the U. S. in 1976), the Bell System is particularly vulnerable to these factors.

The problem had elements of design and of manufacturing. The former focused on providing a cable and connector technology of equivalent electrical, mechanical and reliability in performance to that achieved with copper. The latter focused on developing a manufacturing process as fully compatible as possible with the high speed tandem operations of wire drawing, annealing and insulating, now used for copper. The targets then were equivalent reliability and maximum compatibility.

The problems posed by aluminum itself include:

(a) its lower electrical conductivity ($\leqslant 65\%$ copper standard);

(b) its highly resistive and quick-forming oxide;

(c) its high electropositive potential;

(d) its normally poor combination of strength, ductility and creep resistance when high (>60 per cent copper) electrical conductivity is sought.

These problems are not serious for electric power transmission lines nor for motor and transformer windings when properly designed. Communication cables and building wire do present serious problems arising particularly from (b), (c) and (d).

These difficulties were dealt with in the aluminum-conductor telephone cable as follows.

(a) To meet current cable transmission requirements and provide equivalent copper conductivity, the electrical conductivity of aluminum was specified as 60 per cent copper standard and a 2-gage size larger cross-section was used. (The cable size penalty incurred in adopting aluminum alloys with less than 60 per cent arises not only from larger conductor cross-sections but also from thicker insulation needed to maintain cable capacitance requirements.)

(b) Oxide characteristics required a pressure-type connector capable of providing a gas-tight joint under thermal cycling and conductor creep. This was accomplished with an indium-plated, phosphor bronze, knife-type connector shown to maintain satisfactory contact resistance.

(c) The electrolytic and galvanic corrosion properties of aluminum necessitate exclusion of moisture from the conductor and from connectors where dissimilar metals are in contact. Extruded polyethylene wire insulation forms the primary conductor moisture

barrier; a new cable sheath with a continuous aluminum foil barrier is the second; pressurized gas or petroleum jelly filling in the cable is the third*. The connnector housing is also filled with an organic gel.

(d) Although the strength and ductility of electrical grade aluminum were satisfactory for wire sizes of 17 and 20 gage, a new alloy was required for 24-gage wire. An Al–0.8Fe–0.12Mg alloy was developed for this purpose and subsequently found to have creep properties comparable with tough-pitch copper and far superior to that of electrical grade aluminum.

In the area of processing, the aluminum-alloy producers were convinced of the need to use liquid-metal filtering to achieve low wire breakage on drawing. A new cleaning and induction-annealing procedure was adopted and an H-11 temper (20 per cent reduction in area) was found to give the best combination of strength and ductility.

The aluminum industry was initially reluctant to participate strongly in this program, questioning both the size of the market and the need for further alloy and processing development in this area. When convinced, however, they participated actively, and provided the new Al–Fe–Mg alloy which is now being promoted for this and other electrical applications. The Bell System worked with the major U. S. aluminum producers in this development and the functional interactions were between the working-level plant metallurgists in these organizations. On the producers' side, marketing and sales people provided a strong stimulus when made aware of the market potential, and research people became involved at the later stages to "fine tune" the pragmatic solutions already reached.

There is no unique example of technology transfer either into or out of this case, but several associated technologies, *e.g.* connectors, were affected by the substitution and parallel programs were needed to solve these problems. This lengthened the program's duration (approximately 5 - 6 years) and emphasized critical-path considerations and the desirability of a systems approach. With the solution of the basic problems in an all-aluminum conductor system, the expedient nature of a copper-clad aluminum substitution becomes more apparent.

Polymer Latex-modified Portland Cement**

Concrete and cement is an experience-based industry with long traditions, very high volume and intense pressure on unit cost. An expansion of the

---

*Historical note: In the early 1950's, the Bell System experimented with an aluminum-conductor telephone cable employing paper-pulp-insulated wire. These cables failed catastrophically in the field due to electrolytic corrosion in the presence of the applied voltage and ingressed moisture from cable-sheath damage. This failure posed a psychological barrier to acceptance of the new cable which was only slowly overcome with successful field performance.

**This description is based on information furnished by H. B. Wagner of Drexel University.

polymer field has now touched this long-standing material and is providing new capabilities through polymer latex-modified portland cement. At the same time, new understanding is being generated concerning the fundamental mechanisms of cementitious attachment. Close coupling has been accomplished between academic and industrial investigators in this area.

A polymer latex-modified portland cement is obtained when a part of the water quantity that would be required in mixing a conventional (*i.e.* non-polymer containing) composition is replaced by colloidal polymer latex particles. This modification, with appropriate latexes, is sometimes accompanied by significant alteration of properties in the resultant material as, for example, enhancement of compressive, tensile and shear strength, altered elastic moduli, improved resistance to chemical attack and increased adhesion to various substrates.

In many instances, the increases in tensile strength and bonding characteristics have been so dramatic (as with brick mortars) that new structural designs and fabrication methods become feasible. In other situations, upgraded chemical resistance, or bonding properties, has allowed introduction of portland-cement-base compositions into applications earlier considered impractical. Methods of installation or repair (as with surfacing compositions or precast concrete wall-panel patching) have been made possible or simplified.

Many individuals and many organizations have contributed to the development of polymer latex-modified portland cement. To make the description more explicit and to emphasize certain aspects of MSE, we have chosen to emphasize the contributions of one group. The interdisciplinarity and the coupling between university and industry is illustrated by a listing of the three principal investigators:

Herman B. Wagner, Professor of Chemistry at the Drexel University, a physical chemist experienced in organic polymers and hydraulic cements;

Dallas G. Grenley, a polymer chemist at the Dow Chemical Company, experienced in polymer latex synthesis;

Jerry Isenburg, a physicist at the Dow Chemical Company, specializing in portland cement rheology and scanning electron microscopy.

Each of the above individuals had been intimately acquainted with polymer-modified portland cement compositions for a number of years, from the chemical, engineering and commercial aspects.

When this cement modification program was started in 1961, there was a considerable amount of empirical data relating to such gross variables as identity of the polymer modifier, the level of polymer content and environmental conditions surrounding the cement hydration (hardening) reactions. No mechanism had been established for the observed reinforcements of cement by certain polymers although numerous suggestions had been put forward. This interdisciplinary team set out to establish a more basic understanding of such systems in terms of the physical and chemical interactions between the polymer and cement. Earlier research in physics and chemistry, entirely unrelated to cement technology, provided the necessary experimental tools.

The results obtained up to this time are best presented by reference first to an unmodified cement composition. With a typical portland cement powder, tricalcium silicate and betadicalcium silicate constitute about three-quarters of its weight. Under ordinary temperature conditions, and with only water available, the hydration of these two major constituents is essentially complete within seven days. Hydration of other constituents requires considerably longer for completion. In any case, the "cement gel" that is progressively developed as the product of these hydration reactions comprises chemical species of high specific surface. The new surface area that can ultimately develop may be 500 to 1000 times larger than that of the initial cement grains, and the strength properties of the hardened cement are importantly linked to this increased surface area and to the structure and packing density of the colloidal hydration products.

A polymer latex may be visualized as relatively uniform diameter (*e.g.* 2000 Å) spherical polymer particles colloidally dispersed in water. Here, typically, one-fourth of the volume of the latex would be an organic polymer such as polystyrene and three-fourths of the volume water. Additionally, small concentrations of surfactants, soaps, polymerization initiators and other minor constituents required for manufacture or stabilization of the dispersion are also present. When such a latex is mixed with the cement powder, a fluid suspension of the cement grains is initially obtained. This fluidity is imparted not only by the water but also by the polymer particles which are considerably smaller than the cement grains.

Following this mixing, one might expect or visualize a number of events and effects, including (a) progressive hydration of the cement grains, as with conventional cement; (b) coalescence of the latex particles with one another, as the dispersant water phase is consumed by the cement-hydration reaction; (c) modification of the rate and/or course of the hydration reactions caused by the presence of the polymer latex particles or other constituents of the latex; (d) physical attachment or chemisorption of the latex particles at the surface of the cement grains and/or cement gel; (e) chemical reaction of the polymer latex in this environment, altering the character of the polymer surface presented, etc.

Among the experimental techniques employed in this investigation were transmission and scanning electron microscopy, electron probe, infrared spectroscopy, electrophoresis, BET absorption and radio-isotope tracing. Special techniques and apparatus have been developed by the various investigators to obtain data on coalescence, adhesion, surface adsorption, mortar rheology and engineering properties. As one example, the tremendous depth-of-field of the scanning electron microscope has been exploited in studying the cement structure in convenient steps of magnification from 20 to 100 000×. The morphology of the cement grains is thus found to be altered by the hydration reactions and the various crystalline forms can be observed. The very small latex particles are perfect spheres in the mortar mixes, but upon drying they coalesce to form a continuous film in which the individual particles lose their identity.

The development of polymer coalescence was found to occur gradually, over a period of hours to days, and the structure of the coalesced polymer within these compositions was detailed microscopically and related to the inorganic components. The rate of generation of specific surface area of the cement gel was retarded by some latexes and accelerated by others; ultimately the surface area developed is not affected by the latex type and the chemical structure of the cement gel is comparable.

The enhanced compressive strength observed is primarily the result of densification of the cement gel structure. Tensile and adhesive strength increases, however, are determined by levels of bonding that are affected between cement and aggregate interfaces and within the hardened cement paste; these are specific to the chemical latex employed.

Moduli of elasticity and rupture were found to be related to the extent of cement hydration achieved and to specific effects of the polymer or interfacial adhesion.

A detailed picture of the structural and chemical events which take place when such compositions harden is being assembled, and it is expected that a systematic procedure for developing effective latexes and polymer-modified materials is emerging.

Optical Fiber Lightguides*

The first serious suggestion that optical fibers might be made sufficiently pure and flawless to act as practicable optical waveguides for relatively long distance optical telecommunications was made by two scientists working in an industrial laboratory, Standard Telecommunications Laboratories in England. Subsequently, various organizations successfully pursued the goal of low-loss waveguides in different ways. The Nippon Sheet Glass Company in Japan and the British Post Office both ultimately achieved low-loss fibers in multicomponent, low melting-point glass systems. Corning Glass Works was the first to achieve fibers of sufficiently low loss to demonstrate communications feasibility; they used high-silica glasses and developed a process in which a glass "soot" was deposited on a mandrel, and subsequently transformed into a glass preform by heat treatment. In concurrent work at Bell Laboratories, scientists used a different approach, whose parentage can be sensed in semiconductor device technology: the conventional low throughput heterogeneous chemical vapor deposition, so important in the growth of epitaxial silicon, was modified into a high throughput, homogeneous process. Using this process, high silica preforms were prepared which, when drawn into fibers, yielded fibers having the requisite transmission parameters for use in field trials.

Though the MSE mode operated, with variations, at all the above organizations, the following notes

refer principally to the Bell Labs program. A brief overview of the technical aspects of the materials science and engineering that has gone into optical fibers is detailed elsewhere [98]. The following remarks are confined to underscoring the personnel and institutional aspects of this program.

Communications systems engineers, with backgrounds in electrical engineering and physics, first set basic performance objectives for optical fibers. They pursued analytical studies of optical-waveguide configurations, invented various possible implementations and made preliminary explorations of a number of them. Other scientists with different experience backgrounds, and in different parts of the organization, were drawn into the program. Some, knowledgeable in glass technology, were involved early as might be expected, but it is noteworthy that seminal contributions to the materials technology were eventually made by scientists experienced in inorganic chemistry and physics. The inventions and breakthroughs made by these people in devising suitable glass compositions, and, particularly, ways of preparing preforms using them, served to bring a sharper focus into the whole optical-fiber development. From then on, the program evolved in a much more orderly way: the succeeding technical objectives could be tackled systematically once the principal outlines of the technical approach had been clarified. Absorption losses had to be reduced further; practical ways to build in predetermined radial profiles to the refractive index to minimize dispersion losses had to be devised; means for drawing preforms into fibers had to be carefully engineered so as to avoid contamination, and ways had to be found to ensure that tight dimensional and concentricity tolerances were met; nondamaging methods for coating fibers on-line in the drawing process with protective polymeric materials had to be developed, including exploration of the materials themselves, otherwise the strength of the fibers rapidly deteriorated; ways of packaging individual fibers into multifiber ribbons or bundles had to be invented and developed so as to make cables practicable; the cables required working-out of suitable fiber-splicing and connecting techniques; cables and their fibers had to be able to sustain the mechanical stresses imposed when they are drawn through conduits under city streets, and they also had to be able to withstand the hostile environmental conditions generally found down such conduits and manholes; and all the while the systems engineers and network specialists had to keep reassuring themselves that optical communications would be economic and competitive with other transmission media, such as copper wires and coaxial cables.

The optical cable, perhaps deceptively simple in its appearance, is in fact an exceptionally sophisticated piece of materials science and engineering. It beautifully illustrates many aspects of the description of MSE that is the basis of this paper. For example,

(a) it was a blend of science and experience, with the latter often having to substitute for lack of a sufficiently detailed basic understanding that would have put the materials aspects on a more predictive footing;

(b) it required inputs from many different people, with a wide variety of disciplinary and experience

---

*This example was not covered in the original COSMAT Report, but it is included here because we believe it to be an outstanding as well as very recent illutration of our MSE theme.

backgrounds, and working in many different parts of the overall organization;

(c) it offered numerous needs and opportunities for individual discoveries, contributions, inventions and recognition, and yet at the same time required the constant forming and dissolving of interdisciplinary subtasks;

(d) it presented the constant stimulation that exists in a fluctuating blend of collaboration and competition, both between individuals and between different parts of the overall organization;

(e) it was kept appropriately coherent as a program by the fact that there was a broad but commonly understood mission objective;

(f) it required the presence of a few key individuals to help maintain an appropriate level of coordination among individuals and groups, often quite widely separated geographically, and to ensure that the program objectives were being approached;

(g) it required a reservoir of a wide range of talents on which to draw in different ways and at different times as the program evolved;

(h) it was *not* achieved through the establishment of a monolithic, self-contained optical-fiber organization.

TV Phosphors*

The discovery of an important red phosphor illustrates the wide span of scientific knowledge which is sometimes required in materials research and development and the very close linkage which can be obtained between new scientific understanding and very practical application. Basic studies in support of laser host materials led to the discovery of a commercially significant red phosphor. A central element of this program was the ability of the investigators to pursue and exploit unpredicted observations. The example is chosen to illustrate the particularly close interplay which is sometimes required between materials and design.

In 1961, an interdisciplinary team at General Telephone and Electronics, Inc., developed a new red phosphor material with a redder color and a capability of operation at higher energies. All TV tubes manufactured in the United States now use this phosphor, or rare-earth compounds subsequently developed by other organizations. The host material is yttrium oxide, which is durable and has good optical properties. The activator which fluoresces and emits the desired (red) light is europium, a rare earth. This material has a high efficiency for cathode-ray excitation. A similar oxide, yttrium vanadate (YVO_4), which was recognized as a good phosphor through the yttrium oxide work, has been shown to give an even redder emission color (desirable for TV) although somewhat less efficiently.

Early color TV screens were limited in brightness by the characteristics of the red phosphor. The blue and green phosphors were operated at reduced electron current to balance with the red phosphor which exhibited current saturation and a color short of bright red.

The story of phosphors is a rich one, extending back many decades in fundamental studies of the interaction of light and matter. Throughout the same period, phosphors have played an important technical role, for example in creating luminescence on cathode-ray screens. Even in such a limited field as red phosphors for color TV screens, there has been a wealth of contributions from several major laboratories. A team of workers at the Philips Laboratory independently discovered the potential for color TV applications of europium-doped yttrium oxide phosphors and the related material, gadolinium oxide. Others had independently explored oxy-sulfide systems and had developed the yttrium compound $Y_2O_2S:Eu$. The following is a description of the development work of three individuals at the General Telephone and Electronic Laboratory in Palo Alto, which led to the new red phosphor of commercial importance. While singling out one group has the effect of neglecting the important contributions of others, the intent is to portray as specifically as possible a material development characteristic of MSE and to identify precisely the various elements of the situation. For present purposes, the details of one specific development, which were readily available to us, seem to outweigh the advantage of the usual scientific custom of giving due credit and reference to all significant contributions.

As is generally true in MSE efforts, the people are of central importance. The three principal investigators were:

Robert White, trained in physics, with experience and emphasis on magnetic materials and resonance phenomena;

Kenneth Wickersheim, trained in physics and specialized in optical spectroscopy;

Robert Lefever, trained as an inorganic chemist with considerable experience in materials preparation and crystal growth.

These three individuals, with different backgrounds and different areas of specialization, maintained a high level of interaction on a daily basis. Each of them had an interest in and a detailed knowledge of the other's current programs. Each understood how his work could influence, and could be influenced by, that of the other two.

It is important to note that the studies pursued by these three researchers had as the original objective not the development of new phosphors, but rather the development of suitable host materials for lasers. The rare earths were identified as promising candidates for laser materials because of the sharp line spectra which are characteristic of rare-earth ions. The sharp lines result from emissions in the 4f shell which is shielded from the local environment by the completed 5p shell. It is this same shielding which leads to the close chemical similarity between the rare earths and yet provides a selection of strong optical lines by utilizing different rare earths. There had been some previous experience with rare-earth activators for phosphorescence but much of that had been discouraging. With the insight gained by the work now

---

*Robert Lefever, University of Southern California, furnished much of the information for this account.

being described, it is clear that rare-earth impurities had caused line quenching in some cases and that the host material had not been suitably chosen. It now appeared that the rare-earth oxides in cubic form would be desirable hosts in that the material is refractory, has the proper crystal symmetry and is chemically stable. These physical and chemical properties plus extensive knowledge of material-growth techniques, optical absorption and emission, as well as interaction of dopant atoms with the host lattice, made the rare-earth oxide approach seem promising.

Fortunately all the fundamental science necessary for this development had been completed, and these investigators were familiar with the considerable span of knowledge required for proper pursuit of this materials-development program. In addition, close interplay was achieved between a knowledge of growth of refractory oxides and a knowledge of line-broadening mechanisms which are the principal road block in the achievement of good phosphors.

Lefever had previous experience with the use of flame-fusion (Verneuil) techniques for the production of single crystals of refractory oxides through the growth of refractory oxides for his studies on ferromagnets. The standard Verneuil apparatus is a concentric tube oxy-hydrogen burner in which the center tube is used to supply the raw material for crystal growth and oxygen. From this work and related studies on flux growth of crystals, he gained a detailed understanding of the importance of crystal imperfections and impurities on radiation line widths (in this case, radiating in the radio frequency range). A particular example, discussed later, is the presence of silicon in yttrium–iron garnet which leads to line broadening by an intermediate process. This experience emphasized that specific impurities can be important in an almost unique way when one is considering a particular physical process. It is impossible to eliminate all foreign impurities from a single crystal, but it may be possible to reduce one or two foreign species which are particularly troublesome to an extremely low level.

Phosphorescence is a material phenomenon in which energy introduced into the material by electron bombardment or ultraviolet radiation is partially reemitted over a period of time in the visible spectrum. Normally the light is emitted from impurity atoms which serve as activators. Mechanisms which reduce the efficiency of phosphorescence include poor transfer of the absorbed energy to the activator, nonradiating energy loss from the excited activator and line broadening of the spectrum of the activator atoms.

Line-broadening mechanisms are attributed to many physical processes, the five most important being: crystalline-field splitting, lattice vibrations, exchange forces, magnetic fields, and resonance. Each is considered briefly here. All of these need to be understood in a detailed analysis of the behavior of a particular phosphorescent material. In a solid, the optical emission lines are usually very broad and often indistinguishable because there are so many ways in which the energy levels can be varied by influences from neighboring atoms. This variation is found for

well-defined positions in single crystals. The electron bond to an individual atom can have its energy level changed by a large variety of physical mechanisms, some of which we discuss briefly. The sum of these interactions leads to a statistical distribution of energy for the large number of atoms involved in any real sample, and the result is a broadening of the emission line.

Crystalline-field splitting is the term used to describe variation in energy level due to the interaction between the electric fields in the crystal and a specific electron state or orbit. If the electron state is not spherically symmetrical and if the crystalline field varies along major directions of the lattice, the energy level will depend on the relative orientation between the electron orbit and the crystal. A low-symmetry atomic site can be beneficial when the desired line is forbidden, as is the case in the europium $4f$ shell. Y_2O_3 has two rare-earth acceptor sites, one of moderately high symmetry and one of very low symmetry. This was an important reason for choosing Y_2O_3.

Lattice vibrations are a frequent source of line broadening. The lattice is in a continual state of vibration due to thermally induced stationary mechanical waves. Solid-state physics has developed an elegant way of treating these vibrations in terms of phonons which can be much more readily manipulated theoretically. Phonons are a mechanical analogy to electromagnetic quanta. They represent a discrete energy of activation, and may be thought of as particles in their interaction with other entities such as an electron bound to an atom or an electron in the conduction band of a solid. Phonons are created or destroyed depending on whether energy is added to or taken from the mechanical system, and if they interact with an electron at the time of light emission, the line may be of longer or shorter wavelength depending on whether a phonon is created or destroyed. Y_2O_3 was known from infrared spectroscopy to have a phonon spectrum which couples weakly with photons in the visible region and therefore contributes little line broadening.

Exchange forces which lead to exchange splitting are a purely quantum-mechanical effect which has no classical analog. Fundamental particles, such as the electron, are identical to the extent that there is no observation which can be made to distinguish whether two particles have exchanged places. If two electron orbits share some common space (the wave functions overlap), it is possible for them to exchange positions. The effect on the energy level of each orbit will depend on the relative alignment of the electron spins. This phenomenon is called exchange coupling and is most important in solids when magnetic ions are involved.

Magnetic fields can also change the energy of the electron state. Every electron has an intrinsic spin with which is associated a magnetic moment. The magnetic moment can interact with a magnetic field. In addition, some states of the electron can be thought of as having an associated electric current which interacts with the magnetic field. Magnetic interactions are of course particularly large in materials containing the transition metals such as iron and nickel with their large magnetic moments.

Resonance broadening is an essential concept to understand in studying line radiation from solids. If an electron state is weakly coupled to another of identical frequency, resonance will occur between the two and the electron energy will be perturbed, leading to a broadened line. The General Telephone and Electronics (GTE) group had done a considerable amount of work on ferrites and garnets where resonance is a key phenomenon in line broadening in the radiofrequency spectrum. The work on garnets illustrates the close connection between material preparation and its use: it set the stage for the phosphor development. Wickersheim and Lefever had earlier identified the presence of a silicon impurity in the yttrium–iron garnet at the tetrahedral oxygen. The silicate ion is incorporated in a tetravalent state in contrast to the trivalent cations in the normal host material. The quadrivalent silicon provides a mechanism for incorporation of a compensating divalent ion to maintain charge neutrality. It has been hypothesized that ferrous iron is introduced from the melt to provide the divalent ion. White had recently provided some confirmation of a theory by Kittel, Portis and de Gennes on line broadening of the magnetic resonance which occurs at a few gigahertz. Fe^{2+} is strongly coupled to the magnetic lattice and in turn is coupled to the rare earth ion by resonance. The result is an easy path for draining energy from the activated atom to the lattice. From this experience, the three investigators were well sensitized to the degree to which the nature of the host and impurities might need to be controlled to obtain narrow-line radiation from a rare-earth activator and consequently high efficiency.

The research environment was an important element in this example of MSE. The work was carried out in an industrial laboratory where there was considerable latitude available to the investigators to pursue directions which they believed to be most promising. At the same time, the program was being carried out for an applied purpose. Because of the close relationship between GTE laboratory, in Palo Alto, and Sylvania, an operating Division, it was well known in the laboratory that the TV industry had need for improved colored phosphors for the cathode-ray tubes and the nature of the required improvements. As a result, a span of knowledge was achieved which extended from scientific investigation to commercial application.

There was an extremely close working relationship between the three individuals of different background and training. In particular, there was a thorough understanding of just what materials characteristics were desired and how they should be reflected in the physical properties of the material. This knowledge was not something which was established *a priori* and left fixed through the life of the project. Rather, the close interaction modified and refined the material characteristics and requirements as the project advanced. With respect to the phosphor development, most of the close interaction required had already been accomplished in the garnet work.

Yttrium oxide was chosen as a laser-host candidate for several reasons. First, the symmetry of the crystal sites for europium were known to be of low symmetry, *i.e.* the local crystal fields vary with direction. Low symmetry is desirable because it removes the forbiddenness of some important 4f transitions in the rare earths. Second, Y_2O_3 has a phonon spectrum which couples weakly with the excited levels of the excited europium activator. The weak coupling increases the probability that excitation energy will be emitted optically rather than by transfer to the crystal without optical radiation. Third, Y_2O_3 had already been grown by Lefever; its optical transmission had been measured by Lefever and Wickersheim and was known to be appropriate. Fourth, Y_2O_3 accepts trivalent europium at a trivalent site. In previous laser material, the rare earth had replaced a divalent ion giving rise to charge compensation and therefore a crystal defect for every activator, resulting in line broadening. Y_2O_3:Eu was the only material chosen for initial studies; the extensive and detailed knowledge at hand precluded the need for a systematic empirical search through many materials.

Lefever was able to grow yttrium oxide single crystals with europium doping. In order to do so, he had to develop a modification of the flame-fusion burner, and then in order to prevent cracking of the crystals he devised a technique for protecting the growing crystal with a coating of powder which reduced thermal gradients in the crystal. Both improvements were patentable.

When the first sample of europium-activated yttrium oxide *laser* crystal was examined in the spectrograph under ultraviolet excitation, it was immediately evident to the eye that this was a superior red *phosphor*. Few scientists in any field are privileged to make a discovery in such a dramatic and instantaneous way. Because of the commercial interest in cathode luminescence, apparatus was built to measure the light emitted due to electron bombardment. The europium-doped yttrium oxide was found to emit a red line of brightness comparable with the green phosphor (willemite) under identical excitation conditions. The color was redder than the red TV phosphor in use at that time, accepted high beam currents without saturating, and emitted efficiently even at elevated temperatures.

It is important to remember that the objective of the program was the development of a hardy, sharp-line laser material, a goal that was achieved. However, as a result of understanding the properties of the material and an awareness of technical requirements for improved phosphors, the potential value of Y_2O_3:Eu was immediately recognized and, because of program flexibility, efforts were channeled into further work on the phosphor aspect of the material.

Much work has been done subsequently by others on rare-earth phosphors for TV applications. Such investigations were stimulated in large part by the Palo Alto GTE group and later by studies at Sylvania and the GTE Bayside Laboratories.

Problems and Failures

The conclusion should not be drawn that all programs in materials research and development are successful. Large-scale programes where criticism is most likely to strike are usually embedded in such complex situations that it becomes very difficult, after the fact, to identify the circumstances which blocked success. In some cases, substantial materials development is done in support of a given application; cancellation of the application then calls the materials development into question. A well-known example of this sequence was the major investment in titanium in the 1950's in the United States which had been criticized by some as being unjustified or overly expensive. The titanium program was conceived and conducted in direct response to projected needs of the U. S. Air Force for supersonic aircraft which could not be built with the then-existing materials. By the time a substantial titanium industry had been established, the successful development of intercontinental ballistic missiles superseded the Air Force plans for constructing a new supersonic fleet of aircraft. Hence, the titanium development was left without its largest potential customer. The titanium program itself, nevertheless, appears to have been successful in evolving a new engineering material together with the necessary processing techniques to meet stated performance requirements.

Examples of more recent attention in the materials community, such as the corrosion failure of stainless steels in nuclear reactor heat exchangers or control problems in the San Francisco Bay Area Rapid Transit, are equally complex to the extent that it is not clear whether the associated materials research and development was or was not adequate.

A famous and tragic example of material failure was the metal fatigue experienced in the early commercial jet aircraft. The aluminum alloy used in the fuselage had been analyzed and tested in many ways, but apparently insufficient attention had been given to the precise design details in the ultimate aircraft structure, particularly the influence of the window cutouts on fatigue cracking under the alternate loading and unloading caused by a hunting pressure system.

Another type of failure was experienced in the selection of a stainless steel for a high-pressure bottle in an aerospace application. An alloy was chosen on the basis of its high strength, but its strength suffered from the welding process. A better overall product could have been obtained by the choice of a stainless steel with less strength but superior welding characteristics.

Engineers were surprised with the performance of nickel–brass alloy springs which had been developed for telephone switching equipment. Although these components had received exhaustive environmental testing before they were released to production, the springs installed in new equipment began to fail after a relatively short service time in Los Angeles. Careful "technical detective" work showed that stress-corrosion cracking occurred in the presence of airbone ammonium nitrate in periods of high humidity.

Trouble has been experienced in the space program with solder joints on printed circuit boards. Studies have now shown that cycling between the extreme temperatures in service can cause fatigue cracking of the solder and loss of electrical continuity. Corrosion of aluminum in the presence of water had released hydrogen, which in turn corroded the thick film resistors and lowered their value below that acceptable for performance.

Tinted glasses which are used for absorption of solar radiation have cracked because the stresses created by uneven solar absorption — for example, at a shadow line — have exceeded the tensile strength of the glass.

Polyacetyl plastics have desirable properties, but failures in service have brought out the fact that in the presence of oxides of nitrogen a chemical reaction is catalyzed which severely degrades the material.

In the consumer area, there have been a number of materials developments which have been less than successful. Plastic components of some appliances, particularly refrigerators and vacuum cleaners, have lacked adequate durability. In refrigerators, plastic parts such as doors, shelves, chiller trays and the like have failed in service. In vacuum cleaners, the floor or rug nozzles sometimes broke when the tools were made of plastic. The sealed-rod type of heating element used in most cooking appliances does not always stay sealed. The filler material which is supposed to prevent contact between the heating wire and the outer cover has proved to be hygroscopic, and when the seal fails an electrical leakage path to the outside of the element can create a shock hazard. A more complete analysis of the complex requirements imposed on this filler material in service might have corrected this problem during development.

There are also the failures of omission. The public or the customer often does not know what to ask for because they are unaware of what materials technology may be able to provide. This is in an area in which the materials community could conceivably provide more leadership.

Project SAPPHO [99] in Great Britain has addressed the question of success or failure in industrial innovation in the chemical and scientific instrument industries. Although that study is more general in scope than materials research and development, it seems likely that some of its conclusions are applicable to our interests. One principal conclusion is that the successful innovators have a much better understanding of user needs. In our consideration of materials R & D, this means that the materials developer should establish a thorough understanding of the way in which his materials are to be applied. Too often, inadequacies in materials R & D appear to result from insufficient knowledge of the entire system in which the materials work is embedded.

Another significant conclusion of the SAPPHO study is that success is not so much correlated with institutional size as with the size of the group that worked on the project.

CHAPTER 18. CHARACTERISTICS OF MATERIALS SCIENCE AND ENGINEERING

General

MSE is an arena in which traditional scientific disciplines interact, as appropriate, with engineering disciplines. These interactions are enhanced by common interests in achieving particular technological goals. And increasingly, these goals are being selected from the view point of societal value. Thus, from an overall perspective, MSE has the following prime characteristics: (a) it is a multidisciplinary field embracing an enormous diversity of disciplinary and interdisciplinary activities and programs, and (b) it is science in action to meet man's needs even though, at any given time, a number of the activities in the field may be more curiosity motivated than application oriented.

This multidisciplinary field embraces activities in the traditional single disciplines, including the work of individuals, as well as interdisciplinary activities which, by definition, require the collaboration of two or more individuals. We believe that the need for interdisciplinary projects and programs can only grow in the future if many of the technological problems facing society are to be met.

There are two main modes for MSE: it is *responsive* to specific needs, and it is *creative.*

Viewed as a whole, MSE is science and engineering aimed at satisfying specific needs. In the responsive mode, these needs furnish motivations and establish a climate for close interaction between the materials specialists and the design engineers. This, in turn, facilitates feedback of changed requirements to the materials specialist as his work becomes steadily more refined. The formulation of new materials for medical implants has involved close interplay between clinical experience and material characterization. The development of continuous hot-strip rolling of sheet steel was motivated by the need for lower-cost manufacturing processes. Fundamental studies on electrolytic reactions allowed the discovery of an anodic-protection process which makes it possible to employ carbon steels or stainless steels in handling corrosive media such as hot sulfuric acid.

MSE is also creative. This field of endeavor has its share of individuals with gifted foresight and insight. Knowledge of new advances in scientific understanding, coupled in one individual's mind with knowledge of potential applications, occasionally leads to the evolution of a material with new properties which is then recognized to have wide utility. The early work of Bain and Davenport on the decomposition of austenite led directly to the concept of the hardenability of steel. In another example, Boesch and Slaney were familiar with the original work of Pauling relating the bond between atoms of sigma-forming elements to the average number of electron vacancies in the bonding orbitals of certain elements. They also knew of a formula which Rideout and Beck had derived from this relationship to predict the composition of sigma-forming alloys in certain ternary systems. Starting with this scientific knowledge, Boesch and Slaney were able to produce nickel-based superalloys without the sigma phase and therefore not subject to this cause of time–temperature induced brittleness.

Yet another illustration is the detailed understanding of the exchange-coupling in magnetic systems and the critical influence of minor impurities which has led to the development of superior garnets for utilization as isolators in electronic circuits.

Nature of Materials Research

Our definition of MSE includes both the generation and the application of knowledge about materials. Materials science is usually concerned with the generation part, materials engineering with the application part.

Two of the vital ingredients for viable, healthy MSE are the everpresent needs and areas of application on the one hand, and the generation of new materials and knowledge concerning materials on the other. Continuing societal needs and desires will always provide corresponding applications for new materials developments. But the flow of such new developments would dry up if basic, non-programmatic research in the field of MSE were to be removed. There might be no noticeable effect on the rate of introduction of new technology for several years, but thereafter the technological capability would begin to stagnate. The slowdown would be precipitous in some (not all) of the fast-developing high technology sectors but less so in the low technology sections. However, since the typical time span between the performance of basic research in materials and its eventual usefulness to society is 10 - 20 years, an industry or a nation could be led to a seriously inferior position on this time scale. Such a delay time for the fruits of basic research seems to be intolerable for many industrial managements, governments, and even for the general public, but is relatively short compared with the waiting period for the fruits of research in other fields such as astrophysics and elementary-particle physics.

Consider a scale which extends from the more basic research on properties of certain materials to the routine application of these materials. At the left-hand of the scale are the investigations aimed at understanding and describing the observed materials phenomena. Such programs are typically motivated by the curiosity of the investigator, by his creative insight and by unanswered questions in the field itself. This approach to research has provided a broad and invaluable foundation throughout the field of MSE. It is the basis of better understanding of the properties of many engineering materials and for the more systematic and efficient solutions of materials problems. Not only is basic research the key

to improvement across the whole field, but is often the source of dramatic innovations in the field. The laser could never have been developed by applied science or engineering improvements to incandescent or fluorescent light sources. Basic research may be closely coupled to engineering and development as was true in the early days of the transistor, or it may be very loosely coupled as is the case in some surface research where a considerable buildup of knowledge is required before practical problems in catalysis or surface deterioration can be treated in a systematic way.

At the right-hand end of the aforementioned scale is routine application of engineering materials: for example, those well described in the handbooks and those with a long history of usage. It is also important to recognize that there remain many practical materials problems which will be most efficiently resolved by empirical approaches based on existing knowledge and past experience. It would be a disservice to denigrate this type of activity or to imply that it will no longer make an important contribution to society. Good engineering has the responsibility to reach objectives in a cost-effective way.

Between these two extremes on the scale is a continuum where science blends into engineering and there is often strong interplay between the two. Figure 2 is a simple representation of the change which is taking place along the science–engineering dimension with time. The pertinence of this simple diagram is not always apparent because a scientist may from time to time become interested in an application and may, himself, move into engineering. Similarly, an engineer may find that the most direct route to his application is first the acquisition of new scientific knowledge or understanding, and so he may sometimes perform as a scientist. Although this blending may be somewhat distracting to one who is seeking a simple picture of MSE, it is in fact one of the very important ways in which coupling is effected between science and engineering in the field. In general, such interaction is most efficiently effected by personnel moving from one area to another within the same organization. The most valuable individuals in a research and development organization are usually those who can straddle, both intellectually and in practice, the interface between science and engineering.

The time scale (program duration) often

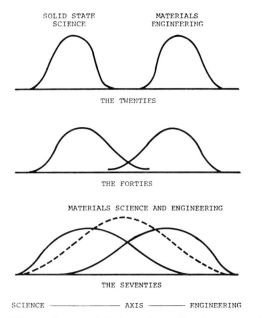

Fig. 2. Change with time of coupling between science and engineering in the materials field.

has a strong influence on the science–engineering dimension. For the most part, very short-term applications are handled by engineering methods, for there is not time available to acquire additional scientific insight; however, exceptions may occur if the applications are exploiting recent discoveries. The early days of the transistor and the laser were examples where close interplay between science and engineering was achieved even though the time for development was short. Well organized materials-development programs with longer than a few years' duration may start with an emphasis on scientific understanding. As such long-term programs progress, the emphasis tends to shift to engineering, and in the final phase, further scientific research may be only very loosely coupled to the engineering work.

In addition to the above operational forces which are serving to shape the role of materials research, there are also significant internal, intellectual forces. It is now recognized that interests in basic phenomena and materials properties transcend the traditional classifications of materials, such as metals, ceramics, plastics, etc. *The unifying theme throughout MSE, which brings together a broad span of activities and a multitude of materials, is the relation between the working properties of a material, or the phenomena that it can exhibit, and its structure and com-*

position — the so-called structure–property–function relationship. The properties are diverse (*e.g.* mechanical, electrical, magnetic, optical, chemical, biological, etc.) and the material types are many, but increasingly the professionals engaged in materials research are acquiring the ability to maneuver in these dimensions in whatever way seems most effective for achieving the desired scientific or technological goal.

Nature of Materials Development, Design and Engineering

Society wants things or services which require materials, but there must be the intermediary of a design or application specialist to transform the materials into a product or service.

Design is used here in the broadest sense of "the process of selecting the means and contriving the elements, steps and procedures for producing what will adequately satisfy some need", or in an engineering context, "the drawing up of specifications as to structure, forms, positions, materials, texture, accessories, decorations in the form of a layout for setting up, building, or fabrication"[100]. The design engineer has broad responsibilities for understanding the nature of the materials utilized. In addition, he has responsibility for quality control and product evaluation.

The contribution of materials development to the public consumer is almost inevitably made through a design or application. There are exceptions such as synthetic sapphire which is marketed directly as a material, but these cases are comparatively rare. Much of the work in materials development is naturally supportive or responsive in that new and demanding designs are frequently limited by available materials or material properties. As a case in point, the designer of a turbine blade for a jet engine would like a very high temperature of operation for thermodynamic efficiency. The need for a high temperature, high strength material for this service was met by the materials community through the development of special alloys with controlled microstructure [101]. The search for higher intensity, more efficient lighting was supported by the development of pore-free aluminum oxide which is highly translucent and yet can contain the high pressure sodium discharge. In the creative mode, materials development is often the key to entirely new designs. Such new capabilities pervade all technology, but two examples will illustrate the point. The one-piece molded fiberglass sailboat which is leak tight and requires little maintenance is a direct consequence of the development of fiberglass. Synthetic diamond research has provided a polycrystalline diamond which enables a major redesign of drill bits for oil-well drilling.

In either mode, whether responsive or creative, the materials development must work through a designer or applications engineer to reach the consumer and connect its contribution to society. Therefore, the interface between the materials developer and the designer is of paramount importance. A methodology or philosophy which has been successful in smoothing this interface is the systems approach. The interdependence of the designer and materials developer is so strong that it is frequently impossible to apportion credit or blame when a program has succeeded or failed. Thus, the materials development specialist has a responsibility to establish close liaison with the design or applications engineer.

A considerable portion of the COSMAT inquiry was devoted to the relationship between materials development and national goals. In some programs, materials development does play an important and even central role, but only in conjunction with other factors. Many examples of both past and possible future programs must necessarily stress the design or application aspect even though we are here primarily concerned with the materials problems. The reason for this is that the device or product constitutes the common ground for linking the materials community and the general public. We recognize that attention to materials problem alone will not normally solve any of the concerns faced by society, nor will exclusive attention to design without adequate materials development. Therefore, we continue to emphasize the inseparable connection between materials development, design, and application.

Systems Approach to Materials Development

Methods of systems planning and systems engineering, in which the repercussions throughout the system of a change introduced at any point in the system are recognized and taken into account, have been highly developed, for example in defense and communications systems. The systems approach is sometimes shrugged off as "just trying to think of everything", but this is essentially what it is, as described more fully below. There are various needs and opportunities for extending this approach in the materials field.

Technological systems of materials

As a technology advances, each material tends to become more highly adapted to its specific role in the end product. These products are composed of systems of materials, each chosen to fit a particular profile of functional properties and environmental requirements. Modern technological machines and devices — nuclear reactors, jet engines, integrated circuits, etc. — consist of intricate, highly interdependent assemblies of materials, each carefully adapted to its specific role in the total structure. Changes made in any one part of the system can have a very significant effect on the performance of the whole system (for example, the development of low-absorption glass fibers which can replace copper cables for communication) and can often necessitate complete redesigns.

Materials cycle

The global materials cycle is also a system in which steps taken at any point can have repercussions (often surprising ones) at other parts of the cycle, as well as having concomitant effects on energy requirements and environmental quality. For example, commercialization of advanced batteries now in development would relieve gasoline demands and reduce smog in commuter areas. The successful demonstration of power generation by thermonuclear fusion or direct conversion of solar energy could cause great changes in the demand and consumption patterns for fossil fuels. In a different dimension, environmental legislation may reduce the use of certain materials currently in high demand (*e.g.* mercury in paper processing and batteries), accelerate use of others (*e.g.* platinum for automobile emission catalysts) and offer increased availability of some (*e.g.* sulfur from stack recovery). One of the most important emerging forces in the materials cycle is the limited availability of certain raw materials. These potential shortages on various time scales have important repercussions throughout the cycle but particularly spotlight a vital role for MSE — to develop substitute materials made from abundant or renewable natural resources and to engineer ways of making do with considerably less of the scarce materials. Thus, the need for concerted approaches wherever possible rather than just haphazard or separate approaches in the materials cycle is becoming more critical.

Methodology

The phrase "systems approach" describes a methodology which has been developed to deal with complex systems comprised of many closely interacting parts. The systems approach provides an effective framework for an undertaking in which many different groups or individuals must make specialized contributions. It is particularly effective in highlighting those critical parts of the program which require particular attention and extra effort. The systems approach has been utilized to deal with a wide variety of problems in technology, business, politics and national security.

In MSE, the systems approach is needed to provide the best match between the materials development and its ultimate application. Rather than start immediately upon a materials development, the MSE practitioner must first analyze how the material is to be employed and for what purposes. This is not a casual question but rather a deep and searching one. The actual function required of the material must be delineated, together with an understanding of the technical and economic tradeoffs between materials properties, processing methods and performance difficulties. This prior understanding of the many factors at play can also lead to the possibility of alternate solutions, so that the result may be creative as well as responsive. During the life of the program, new information will become available as to the practicalities of achieving certain materials properties. This information can be fed back in a meaningful way to the applications designer so that the overall engineering solution can be modified. A typical flow sheet of the overall process is illustrated in Fig. 3.

Contemporary expansions of the systems approach

While systems engineering helps MSE make its contribution to society more effective, it

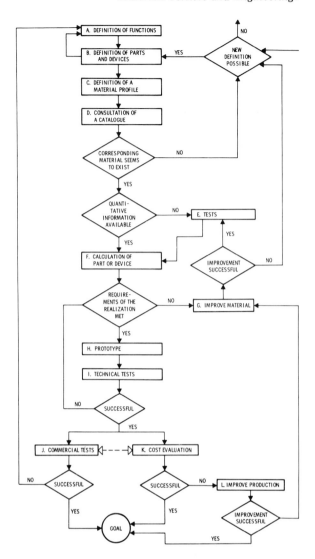

Fig. 3. Example of systems engineering applied to MSE [99].

also seems to be the area where there has been the most difficulty. When we reviewed a number of projects in which MSE failed to live up to expectations, we most frequently found that some aspect of the systems approach was missing.

It is noteworthy that, in the past, most contributions in MSE have neglected one key element of the total system, namely the environmental impact. In selecting or developing materials for a particular application, the material cycle must be kept in mind. To move towards the contemporary goal of environmental quality, materials recycling and disposal must be an important element in materials decisions. With the striking control over materials properties which MSE may provide, there are many trade-offs which can be considered between raw material costs, fabrication, product performance and ease of recycling or disposal. The last two have assumed increasing relevance and must be fully accounted for in future systems considerations by MSE practitioners.

Another growing force in the materials cycle is the supply and demand pattern for energy. This impinges not only on the energy consumption entailed by a new product in its manufacture or service but on all stages of the materials cycle. No major development at one part of the materials cycle can be dealt with in isolation; the consequent impact on energy resources and distribution at other stages of the materials cycle must also be taken into account.

In summary, there will be a growing need in the future to pursue the systems approach both internally and externally in major MSE programs. The complexity of modern technological hardware requires the systems approach on internal materials systems; the mounting problems of resource availability, fuel supplies and environmental quality require the systems approach to be applied to MSE in an external context as well.

Multidisciplinary and Interdisciplinary Activities

We have already noted that the field of MSE is multidisciplinary in that it embraces activities in a wide range of the traditional disciplinary areas, activities which are very often undertaken by individuals. But while much basic research and creative invention may be carried out in the disciplinary mode, within the multidiscipline of MSE there are growing opportunities for various interdisciplinary endeavors in which a variety of specialists, many of whom are also in the forefront of their respective disciplines, interact in achieving progress towards scientific or technological objectives. Without such interaction many well-known achievements, such as the transistor, color phosphors for TV, reactor fuel elements and titanium aircraft skins, would not have been possible.

Even in basic research, with new knowledge as the prime objective, there is increasing awareness of the fact that very often significant progress cannot be made within one discipline alone. It is frequently necessary, instead, for individuals from two or more disciplines to combine their skills, their knowledge and approaches to attain something which none of them could achieve on his own. The bodies of knowledge needed for progress in the materials field are often not congruent with the traditional scientific disciplines. They call more and more for creative cooperation among disciplines — including the physical and life sciences, engineering and the social sciences — in order to carry ideas, discoveries or inventions through to successful application. Interaction, even friction, among specialists from different disciplines is a prime source for the vitality of MSE.

Interdisciplinarity is a practice. Interdisciplinarity cannot readily be measured or quantified; it is an attitude or a way of working, but its mastery is not a self-contained goal as it is in many disciplines. It is an intellectual and adventurous path and those who travel it sense an experience which may have lessons for other spheres of human endeavor. Interdisciplinarity, related mainly to research and development, is a new stage in the evolution of scientific knowledge but it is not necessarily the only way by which science and engineering can advance. Historically, as science broadened it fragmented into separate disciplines; now interdisciplinarity based on close cooperation for a given purpose brings new combinations together. These interdisciplinary combinations may also be transient, fragmenting or disappearing in turn, and so the social organization of technology evolves and adapts to changing interests, needs and priorities; indeed, there is sometimes coalescence into new disciplines. Much of the strength of MSE lies in its flexibility and adaptability which arise from the diversity of talents, viewpoints and knowledge bases.

Interdisciplinarity does not imply any submergence of an individual's personal satisfactions or professional recognition; rather, these may well be enhanced by making his contributions more evident and more widely known. Unlike group efforts in some other fields, MSE projects have the advantage of offering many such opportunities for personal achievement within group endeavors. The synergistic interaction and mutual recognition of the value of each individual's contributions can well lead to accomplishments and an *esprit de corps* which surpass those which any person might reach himself.

We see MSE as becoming increasingly more adaptable to interdisciplinary clusters. At first thought, this would seem to conflict with the role of outstanding individuals, such as Kroll in the making of ductile titanium, Matthias in the creation of many new superconductors, Land in the conception of the synthetic light polarizer, and Baekeland in the invention of Bakelite plastic. Closer examination shows, however, that the creative efforts of these individuals were followed by interdisciplinary team activities in order to bring their inventions to practical fruition. This pattern will continue. We shall always need creative individuals, but in the future they will more likely flourish in a multidisciplinary environment, and they will require the efforts of complementary disciplines in the interdisciplinary modes to complete the innovation.

CHAPTER 19. COUPLING WITHIN THE FIELD OF MATERIALS SCIENCE AND ENGINEERING

As noted, the technological needs of society are generally not congruent with the traditional scientific and engineering disciplines. Nor can they usually be met by engineering alone, but require a balanced range of activities extending from basic research to marketing. Further, there is frequently good reason for coupling the activities of different institutions, academic, governmental and industrial, in order to achieve technological advances. In this chapter, some aspects of coupling among disciplines, activities and institutions will be examined together with factors that influence the effectiveness of such arrangements in MSE.

Coupling, as we usually regard it, applies to mechanisms for promoting cooperation, collaboration and knowledge transfer among individuals, among different parts of an organization and among institutions. In trying to arrive at a description of this multiply connected system, it is helpful to note some important dimensions of MSE.

(a) The time scale for a program may vary from a few months to years.

(b) Geographic coupling may be as close as . the same laboratory or cooperation may extend over continents.

(c) The size of the project may involve one investigator or many.

(d) One project may require a close bridging between science and engineering, while another may involve only one or the other. Some developments in MSE have necessitated contributions from many disciplines; others have been pursued within just one of the classical disciplines.

(e) In some programs involving several people, the interactions have occurred on a person-to-person basis; in other cases, the coordination is effected through organizational arrangements so that the individual investigator need not personally carry out the transfer of his specialized knowledge and findings to other disciplines.

(f) The material of concern may be as simple as a nearly perfect single crystal of one element, or it may be as complex as a composite containing many elements, phases and impurities.

Loosely Coupled Multidisciplinary Activities; Tightly Coupled Interdisciplinary Activities

MSE is a multidisciplinary field within which they are increasing opportunities for interdisciplinary programs and projects. Generally we picture the multidisciplinary activities as "loosely coupled", whereas the interdisciplinary activities are more "tightly coupled".

In the loosely coupled, multidisciplinary mode, organizations may be guided by an overall purpose or theme (see below) which serves as a natural stimulus, a common interest, for bringing about collaboration among professionals in different disciplines in a more-or-less spontaneous way. But it is by no means necessary, or even desirable, for every individual to work in close collaboration with others. Some will do so much of the time, others only part of the time and yet others not at all, each according to his interests and effectiveness. However, the contributions of all are important to the overall purpose of the organization.

An individual working on his own is generating knowledge which others will want to draw on, but he himself may do nothing beyond using the traditional vehicles of talks and publications to see that his knowledge is made available to others. To ensure that this knowledge gets effectively coupled into other projects is then much more the responsibility of the management or sponsors who are presumably aware of what everyone in the organization is doing and why it is being supported. So in this framework, an individual's mode of operation may vary from time to time between disciplinary and interdisciplinary, as he sees fit. In the larger context, the multidisciplinary mode preserves many more of the traditional academic freedoms for the individual than does the interdisciplinary mode. It is particularly suited to the longer term research and development programs (5 - 15 years or more) and is likely to be more acceptable, say, to the academic solid-state science communities than is the interdisciplinary mode. But the multidisciplinary mode is probably also a good description of the inclinations of academic metallurgists and ceramists; for example, the metallurgist studying the principles of spinodal decomposition is probably no more tightly coupled into an overall purpose than the solid-state physicist who is developing a fundamental understanding of the nonlinear optics of a crystal. Both will spend most of their time pursuing their own ideas and researches, but both may eventually recognize the practical implications of their findings and sense when it is likely to be worthwhile to establish contact, and perhaps even short-term collaboration, with professionals who are more application oriented. To help further illustrate the nature of the multidisciplinary mode, essentially all of solid-state physics is vital for MSE, but by no means does this imply that all solid-state physicists are tightly coupled into MSE all the time.

The interdisciplinary mode of collaboration will involve a more tightly coupled group of professionals, drawn together from various disciplines to tackle a specific mission or reach a stated goal. It implies a commitment on the part of the individual to choose his own direction and the corresponding time scale in support of the interdisciplinary group objective. The freedom of the individual has to take second place to the overriding importance of reaching the group's overall objective on time. The individual is constrained to spend a major part, if not all, of his time working on the group project. Obviously, this interdisciplinary mode is more acceptable to those persons who find satisfaction in the cooperative achievements of a group, and is less so to those who value an individual sense of achievement more highly. This interdisciplinary picture is synonymous with the way in which much of industry tackles its development and engineering work. It also is more typical of short-term (*e.g.* up to 5 years) research than of the longer term.

Factors Aiding Interdisciplinary Coupling in Materials Science and Engineering

Individuals from different disciplines can work most effectively with each other if they have languages in common. The materials field provides several such common languages which transcend disciplinary boundaries. These languages provide an intellectual catalyst for interdisciplinary efforts.

The common languages include basic theories and concepts about solids, materials-processing methods, experimental techniques and instrumentation and computer applications. Such languages emphasize the features that are common to metals, ceramics, plastics, electronic materials and natural products. Some examples of these common languages are described below.

Basic theme and concepts

There are some basic physical models of solids which have been shown to apply to many materials. One of the most important of these is the recognition of the defect nature of solids. At one time it was thought that single crystals were nearly perfect geometric arrays of atoms or molecules in the particular structure revealed by X-ray diffraction. Through experiments on single-crystal metals, semiconductors and other work, it has been shown that practically all solid samples contain important defects. Many of the properties, particularly electronic, optical and mechanical, are dominated by the defect structure. The concept of defects in solids is a fundamental building block in understanding the behavior of any solid material. Chemical impurities are a special type of defect. The importance of an impurity in both the chemical and physical behavior of solids has been revealed particularly through the extensive studies of semiconductors and metals, and is now being applied to other materials.

The idea of a band structure is another unifying concept which has been proven in studying many types of materials. Phase relations and thermodynamic equilibrium have also played key roles in greater understanding of conductors and insulators, of alloy systems, and of crystals and amorphous materials. The concepts of nucleation and growth, and of diffusion and segregation are applied to many classes of materials. Investigations on the deformation of metals have provided essential inputs to understanding the deformation of ceramics and glasses. The idea of a domain has played a major role in magnetic and ferroelectric materials which, in turn, may be metallic or ceramic. Another example of a prevailing physical entity is the grain boundary. On its simplest level, the grain boundary is an array of dislocations caused by the intersection of two single-crystal regions oriented at an angle with respect to each other, but it is usually much more complex. Grain boundaries are of special importance in any polycrystalline solid regardless of its material or classification.

Materials preparation

The methods of materials preparation have also been a factor in reducing the differences between the old materials classifications. The development of solid-state devices requiring highly purified materials was built upon the knowledge gained of segregation at a solidification front as studied earlier in metals. Techniques for growth of crystals of one particular type are often shown to have much more general application. The advent of complex materials preparation schemes, *e.g.* the combination of high temperature and high pressure for producing diamonds leads the investigator to search for opportunities to exploit his technique investment in other types of material.

Experimental techniques and instrumentation

Basic science couples very closely with MSE in the area of diagnostic tools for direct measurements of phenomena occurring at the microscopic and atomic levels. In the past, it has been basic research, particularly in all branches of physics, which has given rise to the new and powerful measurement techniques and it is to be expected that this will continue in the future. Many of the newer diagnostic methods are sufficiently difficult to master that individuals may specialize in the technique itself. The unifying influence then results from the natural desire of the investigator to apply his instrumentation to as many different materials as possible.

A related factor bringing together a unifying approach to all materials is that of nondestructive testing and evaluation. Again we see detection methods developed over the past few years which are applicable to many types of materials at every stage of processing or service. Examples are gamma-ray and neutron inspection, helium-leak detection, infrared imaging, holography, ultrasonics and acoustic emission.

Computers

Another development having a strong influence on the unification of MSE is the high speed digital computer. Most materials problems are complex and particularly so if they are involved in engineering application. Only rarely does one encounter a materials problem in which the important phenomena can be treated in a mathematically simple way. As a result, until recently it was necessary to make grossly simplifying assumptions in order to yield a mathematically tractable problem. More often than not, these simplifications were strongly material dependent and, therefore, highly restrictive. With the aid of high speed computation, it is now possible in some cases to start with more fundamental principles and to keep track of many of the complexities of a real material in analyzing its properties in terms of structure and composition. Not only does this elucidate the relation between scientific knowledge and the external behavior of a material, but it also reveals the common dependence of diverse materials on the same scientific models or concepts.

Importance of purpose

A hallmark of a continuingly successful research and development organization is a clear recognition by all concerned of the overall long term purpose, mission, or theme of the organization. Success of inhouse governmental and industrial laboratories in MSE has reflected especially the degree to which the overall mission of the laboratory has been defined, understood and accepted, so as to provide a central interest that draws professionals from different disciplines together and provides continuity in basic studies beyond the span of single development projects.

In striving to follow the overall purpose of an organization, there are usually tempting opportunities into byways which may have to be resisted. Otherwise, the greater goals would become fragmented and the main capability to focus a diversity of knowledge from many fields of science and engineering into a joint effort toward an ultimate goal would be badly obscured.

As Alvin Weinberg, then Director of Oak Ridge National Laboratory, has stated, "A research institution must have a purpose that transcends the individual purposes and aspirations of its scientists; that it can fulfill its purpose only insofar as the separate disciplines and techniques interact with one another to produce more than they could achieve working in monastic isolation".

A clear understanding of the institutional objective on the part of the assembled community is vital, but the objective must be very carefully chosen and stated — it must be sufficiently important, suitably broad and technically meaningful that talented individuals will be inspired by it, challenged to help achieve it and rewarded by a sense of worthwhile accomplishment as progress is made toward the goal. The continuing overall purpose of an organization may well be in the areas of human needs. Themes such as energy, transportation, defense, health services and communications, are broad enough to draw on many disciplines, yet specific enough to give all a sense of mission.

Such themes serve in a variety of ways: they can foster cohesiveness in an organization and help create an *esprit de corps*; they can facilitate decision making as to which course to follow in research, personnel and program planning etc.; they can add even further zest to the most basic of the research activities. The latter point is especially noteworthy in that basic research often flourishes, and even the scientists themselves become specially intrigued, when a connection can be traced between the basic research and important new applications — for example, trying through basic research to determine what sets limits on the superconducting transition temperature of a material is spiced by the realization that a breakthrough in the theory might have tremendous consequences for energy technology.

Interdisciplinary objectives such as those just mentioned, while common in industrial and governmental organizations, are still relatively rare on the university campus. Yet, they would appear to offer challenging and timely opportunities for academic involvement. We suggest that there is an urgent need for university science and engineering departments to devote at least part of their resources to advancing the frontiers of interdisciplinary research and education in areas of technology that relate to societal requirements. There is a need to develop a better balance between the interdisciplinary and the disciplinary activities in academia, and MSE is an excellent case in point.

Many leading investigators in MSE see no reason why the selection of appropriate themes which foster effective interdisciplinary participation should compromise the traditional academic standards of quality and freedom. Interdisciplinary research need not be of inferior quality to the traditional research by an individual — often the converse will be true.

Institutional Aspects of Coupling

Departmental composition

The effectiveness of interdisciplinary MSE is influenced by the climate in which it operates. The climate is set by the organization. The special approach of MSE originated at, and has been most effective in, large research and development organizations in both industry and mission-oriented governmental laboratories. In those establishments, materials developmental problems have been relatively clearly identified and have been closely tied to functions, designs and applications. The management of such organizations has had the flexibility to involve appropriate individuals of various disciplines as required to handle the particular mission. Such goal- or program-oriented institutions do not accept the constraint of organizing by disciplines, but rather are guided by the talent requirements to accomplish the end purpose. Thus, strictly disciplinary groupings in departments tend to be disadvantageous. Functional groups covering a broad range of MSE areas are established which, in turn, couple with project groups aimed at specific objectives.

Geographical barriers

Geographical separation between individuals and groups engaged in MSE programs should be minimized. Wherever there has to be a geographical separation, other ways have to be found for maintaining close communication.

Common management is a frequent mechanism. Frequent travel between locations is a must. Organizational and functional arrangements to be avoided are those which simultaneously create geographical separations and separations by discipline, or by distinction between research and development and engineering.

Size of organization

Small organizations, industrial or governmental, may be able to support only small programs in MSE if the usual economic factors are operating. These small programs then have to be very directly related to the product objectives of the organization if they are to be regarded as cost effective; the outcome of and time scales involved in more basic research programs are generally too uncertain in such situations. But in large establishments engaged in complex technologies, there is a much greater chance that the output from various MSE projects will find applicability somewhere in the range of technological activities that are of concern to the organization. Size is, therefore, an important parameter, particularly as it affords flexibility to form new groups and mixes of personnel as new requirements arise.

However, sheer size of the organization is not a guarantee of success in its various projects. In its study of successes and failures in innovation in the chemical and instrumentation industries, Project SAPPHO [99] revealed that perhaps the most important factor for success was the size of the project group rather than the size of the parent establishment. A large organization spread over many subcritical-size projects could fail; in other words, selectivity and concentration seem desirable, perhaps essential. Clearly, in a small organization, it is critical that the right project be selected, and therein lies the principal risk, whereas in a large organization care must be exercised to see that programs are adequately manned.

A corollary to this discussion is that, generally, small establishments are not justified to engage in basic materials research but have to concentrate on development, engineering and marketing — entrepreneurship. However, to do this still requires individuals who are able to interpret and exploit the results of basic research performed elsewhere.

Member-of-the club principle

For effective communication of knowledge and information between organizations, the receiving institution must be "tuned" to the transmitting institution; it must be staffed with some individuals and support some materials programs rather similar in quality and content to those in the transmitting group. Otherwise, the receiver will be less able to interpret, understand, or exploit any of the information it receives.

By maintaining individuals and programs at the institutional interface, an organization is able to respond quickly to new developments wherever they occur.

By the same token, an institution must generally expect to generate and transmit new information itself if it is to receive information in kind from other sources. Thus, an institution that performs and publishes the results of basic research is, in effect, paying its "subscription" to the national and even international basic research "club". By so doing, the institution puts itself in a position more rapidly to assimilate and exploit new research findings the moment they appear. By not paying its "subscription", an organization will tend to trail behind those that do, often having to rely on patent right and royalty negotiations rather than on original invention for its economic health.

While the above remarks are couched in institutional terms, they apply equally to nations as well. National efforts in the many aspects of MSE are vital if a country is to maintain its position vis-à-vis other countries with such competences.

This principle also applies to the industry–university interface. If industry is to make best use of the fruits of basic research in the universities, it must undertake some comparable programs itself. Failure to do so can lead towards two non-communicating cultures.

Some Human Aspects of Coupling
Key individual

A study made in 1966 and reported in *Principles of Research–Engineering Interaction* [103] identified the importance of a "key individual". In a detailed analysis of a number of case histories, the Tanenbaum Committee found that one of the most common elements in programs of successful innovation and transfer of technology to practical application was a key individual. This individual played the role of champion for a particular idea or cause, and appeared to be a necessary, if not a sufficient, factor for overall success in the program.

In reviewing successful examples of materials research and development, we also find that the key individual is important. To achieve coupling between science and engineering or among different disciplines, some one champion has to have the interest, understanding and ability to span the entire program with some minimum level of competence in all sectors. The technical contributions in materials research and development are normally made by professionals who are highly specialized in a particular discipline. The additional element in materials research and development is that the same individual must also develop some appreciation for, and perhaps understanding of, the contributions needed from other disciplines to solve the common problem. If a given program is large, requiring several individuals in the materials and applications groups, or if the mission is of such a nature as to require a wide spectrum of disciplines, then the key individual must have an unusually broad range of interests and knowledge. Therefore, at least one individual in the group must have an intimate understanding of the overall program and how the various elements will combine for the ultimate solution. It is tempting to assume that here is the proper place for a generalist. In practice, however, we find that the key individual is usually himself very competent in some specialized field, but in addition he has made an effort to understand in some depth the nature of the problem and the character of the contributions required from each of the disciplines involved. At the same time, the key individual, if a scientist, should also appreciate the engineering constraints, or if an engineer, be conversant with the underlying scientific aspects of the problem.

Throughout this paper, we have emphasized the coupled nature of materials research and development and the crucial importance of contributions from various disciplines. While recognizing the advantages of such a group effort, we must at the same time note the irreplaceable value of a spectrum of knowledge and understanding in one mind. That "one mind" seems to identify the key individual in materials research and development.

Personal satisfaction

The practical problems of the materials world are complex and normally require the insight provided by more than one specialty or discipline. Furthermore, the interaction between two or more disciplines can establish a synergistic climate for creativity. As already pointed out, success of the interdisciplinary group depends very much on a clear definition or a well-defined common goal and its acceptance by the group members. But in addition, it is also desirable to manage the effort in such a way that each professional member is in a position to make an individual and identifiable contribution in his own specialty.

All members of the group should have some breadth of view and appreciation for the importance of contributions being made by other specialists. Even to the extent that any member prefers to maintain his disciplinary identity, he is likely to be better motivated if he sees the possibility of receiving recognition for his personal contribution.

Nature of groupings

There is danger of confusing the team approach which is characteristic of any large development or engineering program with the interdisciplinary approach characteristic of materials research and development. For a large project which must be completed in a limited time, it is necessary to organize a team of individuals in order that the job can be accomplished. The requirement may simply be one of assigning sufficient manpower to complete the total work in the given time. An example might be the development of a new computer software system. This might be accomplished by appointing a lead system programmer and assigning a number of other programmers to support him by carrying various parts of the overall project. Similarly, in preparing the plans for a large building, the job could be broken down so that one architect might be responsible for one part of the project, another architect for another part and so on. One can readily think of other examples where development requires a team approach in which all the personnel are of essentially the same discipline.

Materials research and development is also normally carried out in a group approach. It is often associated with development programs whose magnitude and time scales require a number of individuals to complete the job within the allocated time. What is special about materials research and development, however, is that different disciplines must usually be focused on the same problem in order to achieve a solution. The difference between the team approach and materials research and development becomes most apparent in the extreme of small groups. In the samll group limit, namely two persons, the team approach often has two individuals of the same discipline and training: for example, two aerodynamicists or two chemists. Materials research and development, in contrast, tends to converge on two individuals with different disciplines and training. Examples of such pairs are a physicist and a metallurgist, an aerodynamicist and a thermochemist, an electrical engineer and an inorganic chemist, a metallurgist and a structural engineer. Thus, it is the interdisciplinary element which is important, not just the combination of two or more individuals.

Supervision of group

The question of leadership or supervision of an interdisciplinary group deserves much emphasis, but at the same time is hard to describe precisely. Supervision of a research and development activity is difficult, but that of materials research and development has an added dimension of challenge.

In a typical development program, the project is organized under a project leader and consists of several professionals to accomplish the objectives in the time allotted. The supervisor must himself be technically competent, must be sensitive to the originality and judgment of the members of his group, and should have that indefinable quality which provides leadership rather than just direction. Nevertheless, in such a group there is a clear understanding of a supervisory–subordinate relationship. In the case of interdisciplinary materials research and development, the added complexity derives from the need for a group to act as an individual. No longer is there the neat arrangement of a project leader, but rather a way must be found so that the inputs from several members can have even weight. This requirement for a true group effort results from the very nature of the interdisciplinary problem which demands significant inputs from two or more disciplines. The very

quality most needed can be destroyed by an insensitive attempt to "direct" the work for more "efficiency".

Coupling through mobility of personnel

Coupling between organizations or between separate locations within the organization is a critical problem in materials research and development. Without question, the most effective coupling between separate groups has been accomplished by the movement of knowledgeable and involved individuals. Although the documentation and publication record is good in materials research and development, there is no way to transmit on paper the many subtleties and sensitivities connected with the processes for producing new materials with special properties. Experience has repeatedly shown that a complex new materials process developed at one site can more easily be transferred to a different manufacturing location if some of the key individuals are also transferred. When that is not possible, special attention must be taken to assure adequate transfer of technology from one site to another. Industrial organizations and governmental agencies solve this problem by first defining clearly the required objectives, second by supporting extensive travel between the two sites, and third by applying special management effort. The experience of the U.S. Advanced Research Projects Agency university–industrial coupling programs illustrates the difficulty of achieving effective interaction when compelling objectives common to the two locations are missing and where there is little or no personnel movement. The problems experienced in such programs do not in any way reduce the need for more effective cooperation between university and industry. It does emphasize, however, that coupling is something more than just good technical work. Attention must also be paid to perceptive management, to acceptance of common goals and to the period required for person-to-person contacts and intergroup working arrangements to mature. Further experiments on university–industry coupling are urgently needed.

There are good examples of close coupling between materials research and development and the design or application engineers in industry and government. On campus, however, this coupling tends to be weak. The traditional academic structure, with departments aligned according to disciplines, militates against this type of coupling and there is normally no funding to support joint efforts by the materials and design sectors of the faculty. Ways should be found to try block funding for two or three faculty members in a joint effort to link materials development with design for a specific product or service.

Consulting arrangements have been helpful in coupling university-generated knowledge to industry and governmental agencies. Joint appointments, where the same individual works both on and off campus, may be even more effective. The industrial community in materials research and development appears only weakly coupled to academia, partly because of the relatively small numbers of experienced materials-development people who participate in regular faculty activities.

Roadblocks to effective coupling

Many of the obstacles to effective coupling can be inferred from the preceding sections, but a few additional comments are in order.

In the early stages of an interdisciplinary materials program, the group may be composed mainly of basic-research scientists with a relatively small number of engineers. As the project progresses towards application, more engineers may join the group while the basic-research scientists may drop off and move on to other programs. Such an evolutionary sequence in the research and development spectrum provides a very effective way for surmounting the "not invented here" syndrome so often characteristic of programs in which the research, development and engineering are done in sequential stages by different groups or departments.

The literature on interdisciplinary research contains discussions of other roadblocks too, as well as the strengths and weaknesses of interdisciplinarity. A particularly useful summary of the pros and cons appears in *Interdisciplinary Research — An Exploration of Public Policy Issues* [104]. Though the study is primarily concerned with the problems of interdisciplinary research involving both the physical and the social sciences, many of the conclusions reached there are directly applicable to MSE.

CHAPTER 20. IMPLICATIONS OF MATERIALS SCIENCE AND ENGINEERING FOR UNIVERSITIES

Education in Materials Science and Engineering

Every professional field requires individuals of high caliber in intelligence, insight, creativity and motivation; MSE is no different. In practice, however, it must operate successfully with its fair share of the distribution of the available talents among professional people. The more meaningful question then becomes, "What training and experience can be expected to supply effective contributors in the field of MSE?"

Materials development is complex. In spite of the success of science in helping to unify the field, there still remains essential empirical knowledge which must be known by the practitioner. Furthermore, as we have seen, an individual knowledgeable in one aspect of the materials field must have a good working appreciation for the contributions which can be made by other disciplines and specialties.

We have repeatedly emphasized the multidisciplinary and interdisciplinary nature of MSE and the requirement for individual contributors to be well grounded in particular areas. Metallurgy, ceramics and polymerics appear to be merging toward a common discipline; but the range of materials problems faced by MSE is so vast that other disciplines such as electrical engineering, structural mechanics, physics, chemistry, medicine and biology will continue to contribute in many important ways.

To illustrate the varied concepts and viewpoints which different disciplines bring to a problem, Table 3 lists a number of characteristics or attributes which are commonly associated with three disciplinary fields. From this listing, it is obviously unreasonable to expect one individual fully to absorb all of these different viewpoints and concepts to the degree that he can compete with specialists in any one field. Moreover, these are not the only disciplines which contribute to MSE; Table 3 is not meant to be restrictive or exclusive but only tries to illustrate the differences among disciplines.

It is helpful to distinguish between those individuals who generate new knowledge in MSE and those who apply such knowledge. There is a basic difference between these two

TABLE 3
Comparative characteristics and attributes of some disciplines involved in MSE

Those trained in physics tend to	Those trained in chemistry tend to	Those trained in materials, metals, ceramics and polymers tend to
Isolate the problem until it is susceptible to quantitative treatment.	Use some theoretical models, but depend more on correlations, classifications and comparisons to deal with chemical problems.	Accept complex problems associated with practical needs.
Seek rigorous treatment of relatively simple systems.	Accept a relaxation of rigor necessary to allow treatment of complex systems.	Adapt theory from physics and chemistry but add empirical approach to achieve results.
Propose theoretical hypotheses to be followed by experiment.	Place emphasis on experiment; theories often phenomenological.	Make extensive observations followed by empirical relationships, rules and theories.
Know a few basic concepts applicable to many phenomena and relationships.	Use basic concepts plus laws on composition, thermodynamics and kinetics (statistical wiping-out of detail).	Use elemental concepts plus general guiding principles or rules plus experience and knowledge of material classes.
Use zero-order approximations or idealized representations to identify important factors.	Use models plus intuitive reasoning based on experience.	Deal with multiphases, partial crystallinity, grain size, texture, defects and thermomechanical history.
Have confidence to attack any physical science problem.	Have knowledge and experience to solve chemical-related problems in the most efficient way.	Have the interest, knowledge and experience to solve practical problems within time and budget limitations.
Center interest on how or why something happens.	Emphasize the *material*.	Place emphasis on the material, including practical matters of manufacturing.
Assume engineering can be accomplished.	Be interested in how or why, but oriented to application more than basic understanding.	Be interested in utility; desire to deal with real-world problems.
Respond to materials at an intellectual level.	Gain satisfaction in creating materials with new properties.	Have an aesthetic or sensual relation to materials.

activities and that difference will be reflected in the training which is appropriate.

The *creation of new knowledge* implies that the investigator is fully informed of preceding work which has been done in his specialty. In addition, he must have mastery of analytical and experimental techniques peculiarly suited to his line of investigation and, above all, the capability for careful measurements followed by detailed analysis and intellectual scrutiny. Therefore, the logical preparation for a substantial number of contributors in the future will be at the doctoral level. The heavy content of science in MSE makes the higher level degree a natural training route for those who will attack the most basic problems in the field. During the past two decades, academia has been remarkably effective in preparing individuals for careers in materials science by training at the masters, doctoral and postdoctoral levels. The establishment and governmental support of the interdisciplinary materials research laboratories played a central role in this response of the universities to emerging needs of sophisticated technology. The high level of accomplishment in materials science needs to be maintained, but it is also time to recognize that the whole spectrum of MSE should be fully reflected in the academic educational program. In particular, materials engineering now requires similar upgrading, emphasis on interdisciplinarity and major facility investment which materials science has enjoyed through the stimuli of the interdisciplinary laboratory programs.

An individual whose principal function is the *application of knowledge* relating structure, properties and processing to materials function and performance can contribute with a broader and less specialized training. His aim is to understand existing knowledge in MSE and to determine how it can be applied to new products and designs. In such an objective he will naturally be more oriented toward processing and engineering applications across the entire field of materials. The larger share of practitioners in MSE are found in this category because new knowledge in the field can be appropriately applied in many different situations. The generalist is particularly suitable for the smaller companies which do not have the resources to develop new materials properties as a normal part of product development. Because of the breadth and complexity of MSE, the masters level has become appropriate for those who will be mainly concerned with applications in the field, but even here there is increasing attention to doctoral programs.

Because MSE, in the main, is a purposeful endeavor, it is desirable that students slated for advanced degrees should acquire some working contact with practical materials problems during the course of their education. One method which has worked well is the cooperative program in which a student alternates between an industrial job and a period on campus. This scheme has been used primarily at the undergraduate level where the candidate may still be limited in the skills which he can apply to a technical assignment. Nevertheless, most graduates of such programs feel strongly that they were benefited in understanding how their academic training could be put to use.

Another excellent way for a student to gain some firsthand insight into practical problems is summer employment in an industrial or governmental laboratory. This can be accomplished when the student is further along in his academic training and can contribute more effectively. The completion of the B. S. or the first summer in graduate work may be convenient break points for such temporary employment. It is hampered to some extent by both students and faculty who regard the summer away from campus as an interruption in the graduate program. A broader view might suggest that this work experience is an integral part of the educational process in MSE, and should be balanced with the academic courses and research training on the campus.

Unfortunately, summer programs for student work experience in governmental and industrial laboratories typically suffer severe cutbacks during economic recessions. Yet, this in no way reduces the importance of this educational component. Substantial effort should be devoted to creating opportunities for MSE students to gain practical experience before completion of their academic training.

University Research in Materials Science and Engineering

The materials research performance of the universities in this country has been mixed. The output of fundamental materials science in academia has in the aggregate been excellent. However, materials research in the interdisciplinary mode has not faired quite so well when compared with the better industrial and governmental laboratories. The universities have two cardinal principles which interfere with interdisciplinary materials research on campus, and each is securely based on centuries of experience in education. The first is the organization of the university by branches of learning, in other words, by disciplines. Once the disciplines such as physics, chemistry, or metallurgy have been established, the very natures of organizational structures and human beings are such that close cooperation within a discipline is more easily accomplished than across disciplines. In addition, the main peer groups off-campus are the technical societies which tend to be discipline oriented. Thus, both peer evaluation and rewards tend to be structured along disciplinary lines.

The second principle on campus is the preeminence of individual contribution. Academic scholarship and creativitiy are most easily identified and evaluated when they can be attributed to a single individual. In contrast, for many problems originating in nature and in society, such as frequently in MSE, a joint effort may be required for effective solution and the campus has not been a ready setting for such an arrangement. If materials research is to be adequately performed at the universities, then some modifications in the funding, traditions and reward system are required. However if the universities are to serve mainly as training grounds for professionals in MSE, then simply a change in emphasis and motivation may be required.

Materials research is generally interdisciplinary in nature when conducted in industrial and governmental laboratories. Materials research centers on campus, therefore, are ideally situated for bridging between the traditional discipline-oriented activities of universities and the interdisciplinary activities outside the campus. But too frequently these laboratories have failed to take advantage of their opportunities along these lines. Instead, they have often served to provide additional support on campus to the traditional activities organized by discipline. For example, central facilities such as electron microscopes and crystal-growing facilities are not being used in an interdisciplinary way if physicists, chemists,

metallurgists and so on, simply take turns at using them rather than apply them to truly collaborative researches. A major aim of materials research laboratories should be to provide opportunities for members from the various disciplines to undertake, *when appropriate*, interdisciplinary collaborative programs; but by no means should every individual be required to engage in interdisciplinary work all the time.

Materials research centers can offer an effective meeting ground for professionals of different disciplines where joint programs can be initiated and research results obtained which none alone could achieve. A good stimulus for such collaborative efforts is for the center, or a section of it, to have a broad technological focus which serves to promote a common interest among individuals from different scientific and engineering disciplines. Some centers may choose to concentrate on electronic materials and relate to the electrical engineering departments, others on biomaterials and relate to medical departments. Still others may elect broad themes such as energy or communications. When astutely chosen, such themes can embrace a wide range of scientific and engineering activities; they are not unduly restrictive but stimulate further intellectual interactions, and for those who desire it (possibly a growing proportion) they provide a connecting thread between pure scientific endeavor on the one hand and identified usefulness to society on the other. We feel that universities possess, with their materials research centers vehicles that offer exciting opportunities for interplay between traditional academic pursuits and societal needs. It is important to insure that such laboratories make the most of these opportunities.

Funding and Reward Mechanisms

In the traditional academic departments, it is usual for individual faculty members to seek their own research grants and contracts. This practice is less effective in interdisciplinary research projects which are more subject to changing external requirements. A valuable support mechanism for such programs is forward block funding administered by local laboratory management and subject to outside review. Block funding provides flexibility for adapting to the varying needs of different interdisciplinary programs and also provides a source of seed money for new research ventures.

It is important to the success of interdisciplinary programs that there be recognition and reward schemes which compare with those accorded the traditional disciplinary areas. Universities appear to have much to work out in this respect and are generally behind their industrial counterparts.

CHAPTER 21. NEW OPPORTUNITIES FOR MATERIALS SCIENCE AND ENGINEERING

Outputs of Materials Science and Engineering

What are the outputs of MSE? First, and most obviously, the answer is new materials, new processes, new materials systems and improvements in the existing technology and cost effectiveness of materials. Whether in its creative or responsive mode, MSE has an overall major objective in developing materials which meet particular application requirements or open up new application opportunities.

Secondly, MSE strives for additional understanding of materials and the way the materials field operates.

A third output of MSE is the identification or stimulation of an area for expanded fundamental research. Sometimes the work being done to meet particular goals uncovers a materials phenomenon which had not been previously reported and which cannot be readily understood. Still another way in which MSE can stimulate fundamental research lies in the creation of new techniques, instruments or machines for the processing of certain materials.

Fourth, MSE also has a widespread output in the more efficient design or improved performance of many existing products. This transfer of a capability designed for one program to another application is a form of spin-off.

Fifth, MSE has even generated entire consumer industries. One of the most dramatic is the synthetic-fiber industry which now outproduces the combined output of cotton and wool in the United States. Of equal importance is the synthetic-plastics industry to which MSE has contributed heavily. Another large and growing sector is the solid-state electronics industry, whose origin rests squarely on MSE. Still another relatively new and rapidly expanding development is the office copying machine. The development of the electrostatic photocopying surface fully meets all of our criteria for the definition of MSE. the tape-recording industry is another example of the creation of new commercial activity which rests upon the development of novel material capabilities. This has benefited the music world, both in radio transmission and in home reproduction systems. MSE has also played a vital role in large-scale computer systems as well as in the television industry.

Given the various impacts that can result from MSE, it is of interest to look to the future and to suggest ways in which MSE may contribute even further to man's needs.

Changing Nature of Materials Science and Engineering

Like all science, engineering and technology, MSE is changing rapidly with time. It is necessary that we identify the trends in the materials field in order that we can project ahead into the coming years. Our study has revealed the growing incidence of interdisciplinary projects in MSE. A few decades ago there were isolated instances of such work; in recent years, examples have been more frequent. We believe that an important trend has been established; a trend which is likely to be accelerated.

Review of a number of case histories in MSE has shown that science-intensive programs have been the most attractive candidates for the practice of this interdisciplinary mode. Such programs have had two characteristics in common. (a) The projects had established overall objectives which could not be met with existing materials. Objectives of this type have categorical success or failure significance, and are to be contrasted with many programs in which materials development might make only an incremental contribution to better performance or lower cost. Examples which come immediately to mind are nuclear-reactor fuel elements for which materials and methods had to be devised to contain radioactive products, and the oft-cited transistor program which required an entirely new level of semiconductor chemical purity and single-crystal perfection. (b) A second feature of the science-intensive programs has been the need for the entire effort to move out beyond the state-of-the-art engineering achievements;

innovative approaches were required. This created a climate of more open consideration of novel ideas, concepts, developments and changes. Within this open framework, the materials specialists were in a better position to interact strongly with the applications engineers and to make the kinds of trade-offs which have been described here earlier under the systems approach.

This interdisciplinary mode, however, has not existed solely in the glamour projects. In some instances we find individual companies or sectors of the economy where a challenging new goal has been internally generated and where these internal goals have been sufficiently demanding to require a science-intensive approach for their solution. Some examples are the development of polymer-coated razor blades, the creation of the synthetic fiber industry and the integrated-circuit business.

In reviewing the trends of MSE, one must conclude that the contributions to society have been considerable but uneven, *i.e.* some have been served much more satisfactorily than others. One of the themes which emerged in the COSMAT study is that MSE is motivated by, and is responsive to, societal needs. In some cases, specific needs have led to increased scientific investigation and understanding as, for example, in the problem of oxidation and corrosion of alloys. But scientists often prefer to work on problems which yield good opportunities for scientific advances *per se*, and societal requirements may prove too complex to offer much promise of scientific reward. In such instances, the empirical approach or merely dependence upon past experience has had to suffice.

If we now look to the future of MSE, it is clear that several factors combine to continue and possibly accelerate the trend toward the interdisciplinary approach which has already been established. First of all, we are rapidly obtaining greater scientific knowledge and capability, especially in the fields that apply to materials. Since science feeds on its own previously acquired knowledge, this buildup in understanding is an autocatalytic phenomenon and provides a common language which further links the various parts of the materials field. The eventual result will be a science and engineering of materials which is capable of handling a much broader range of problems, even those of societal complexity.

At the same time that the capabilities of MSE are rising, the manufacturer of any product is under pressure from many quarters to squeeze more performance and cost out of his materials. He is asked to hold prices in the face of rising labor costs, to process materials with minimal hazard and pollution, to satisfy increasing customer demands for product quality and reliability and to relieve pressure on dwindling sources of raw materials. In more and more cases, these conflicting demands will result in a requirement for new material or process capabilities. As time goes on, it is likely that some of the industries which are now clearly experience based will be forced to rebuild on a science base. Historically, new knowledge has diffused into old fields. However, if there are experience-based industries in which the old ways are too firmly entrenched, the science-based approach will tend to enter by some other industrial segment taking over.

Increased costs will undoubtedly exert a strong influence on the activities in MSE. Dependence on materials resources and processes which are labor intensive will inevitably decline over the years. The ever-increasing cost of individual repair work will lead to emphasis on material properties not only for first manufacture but also subsequent durability. Similarly, it may be expected that designs will be modified to facilitate easy repair by the user.

Thus, all indicators seem to point to increasing attention to materials development which makes maximum usage of scientific understanding closely integrated with design and application in the broad sense, and which is fully balanced with regard to the overall materials cycle.

Changing Industrial Scene for Materials Science and Engineering

Many of the outstanding advances in MSE have been achieved by industrial organizations making it a practice to support comprehensive and suitably coupled research and development programs. Such industrial accomplishments, as we have noted, include the discovery and subsequent development of nylon, the transistor, the high field superconductor, the laser, color phosphors for TV, high strength magnetic alloys, magnetic ferrites (Netherlands), polyethylene (U. K.), and so on. What is noticeable about these break-throughs is that they took place in companies that supplemented the traditional, experience-based approach to materials and product development with science-intensive research programs aimed at building the body of knowledge on which the new technology was ultimately to be based. These companies established leadership, both for themselves and for their countries, by not leaving this vital longer-range activity to other industries or laboratories, whether domestic or foreign.

With the broadening emphasis on national goals — from aerospace, defense and nuclear energy to more civilian-oriented technologies — the practical objectives of industry are changing, but there is no evidence whatsoever that the importance and value of research will be diminished. Enough basis is presented throughout this paper to point-up the many fresh technical challenges facing industry beyond those which arise directly from the growing problems of materials availability, energy cost and concern over environmental quality. Many of the newer challenges can be met only with the help of a sustained, science-intensive approach; reliance cannot be placed solely on the experience-intensive approach. Indeed, often there is no such experience.

Yet, despite the proven long term values of comprehensive in-house research and development, the pressures of competition from other companies and other countries will invariably force management's attention to the short term. The recent trend, particularly in the late 1960's and early 1970's, has been to reduce bottom-line costs by cutting back on relatively long range research and development, even in the science-intensive industries. Such cut-backs have been even more severe in the experience-based sector; the relatively basic research done there has been eliminated in many instances. Of course, cutting back on research and development may improve a company's profit position in the short run, but it leads the company and the entire industry into a less dynamic and less innovative position in the long run. However, the company that continues to perform research and development may even see itself priced out of an eventual market by those companies who simply avoided research and development costs and went directly into production using the results of other companies. Because of

such circumstances, there is a growing attitude that the penalties for failure in a research and development program are too costly, while the rewards for success are too easily appropriated by others and hence too uncertain. For the company not in a position of leadership, it often makes most sense to obtain its new technology from other sources through cross-licensing or royalty agreements, for example; but for the company that is striving for leadership, investment in a balanced research and development program is vital. The same pattern has been emerging on an international scale; while it was in the catching-up phase, Japan imported many of its new technological ideas. Now that it has caught up in many areas and is aiming at leadership, Japan is investing more heavily in research and development.

All programs in technology are influenced of course by the magnitude and arrangement of financial support. One such aspect of MSE needs special emphasis. The most critical stage in the development of any new material is in its transfer from the research and development laboratory to full-scale production and utilization. Successful transfer of this type is a prerequisite for the contribution of any new material to society. At the same time, this transfer process is normally the most expensive phase of the entire innovation. Moreover, the depressed industries are often those which are in greatest need of innovation in materials and manufacturing processes. This means that new ways must be found to promote the implementation of new manufacturing processes which can yield significant economic or environmental advantages. Added incentives are needed which on the one hand reflect the broader perspective of the nation, and on the other hand retain the insight of a profit-oriented company. Plant investments for new materials and processes are normally major expenditures and the decision to commit resources for these purposes requires a climate which is attractive to significant risk taking.

Changing Societal Goals and Support-base for Materials Science and Engineering

At any given time, a society or a country has a number of goals which receive priority. The method for establishing these goals is not precise, but, nevertheless, a general consensus is somehow reached. The selected goals are a way of drawing attention to programs which require adequate allocation of resources and contributions from many segments of national life. Frequently, the attainment of such goals depends on a strong technological input. In the period following World War II, the development of weapons, both nuclear and conventional, received high priority in the United States. After Sputnik, the demonstration of technological excellence through the man-in-space project became a goal of the United States. More recently, emphasis has shifted toward goals which more directly affect the daily lives of the general population such as energy, health care, transportation, environmental quality, housing and urban renewal. Dramatic progress in meeting these goals can only be achieved through considerable innovation and much of that innovation will be in materials technology.

Innovation is one factor which has traditionally provided countries with economic leadership in the world markets and with a rising standard of living at home. For example, in the United States, innovation has spawned a number of science-intensive industries such as television, aircraft, computers and plastics. Innovation has also augmented economic strength by advances within established industries such as communication by microwave links, wrinkle-resistant fabrics, self-developing photography and prestressed concrete. In most cases, innovation includes the development or modification of key materials.

More and more frequently, interdisciplinary research, development and engineering is proving to be the most successful, often necessary, approach to innovation. Opportunities for the lone inventor are relatively limited, as evidenced by the percentage of patents granted to individuals not affiliated with a large company. In 1901, independent investigators obtained 82% of all patents; in 1967, their share was only 23.4% [105]. The sophistication of modern technology increasingly requires a group effort in which participants — each with specialized training and knowledge — jointly achieve innovation of significant impact. Therefore, successful practice of the interdisciplinary approach deserves special attention.

We believe that MSE will continue to play an important role in meeting societal goals. It will often be a cardinal element in innovation,

particularly in matters bearing upon energy resources, environmental control and economic strength. In many instances, MSE has demonstrated the power of an interdisciplinary approach to solve difficult problems. Most of these examples are found in science-intensive technology programs. That is where the performance requirements on materials have been sufficiently crucial to demand the science-intensive approach for the adequate solution. Moreover, in many of these activities, the customer has been the government rather than the public market and cost considerations have played a different role. It is interesting to note that the science-intensive technologies are relatively new; typically, there is no long established body of knowledge and well-identified group of practitioners. Rather, the nature of the problem causes a new cohesion to be formed. It is in this situation that the highest reception prevails for new ideas, new approaches and the maximum utilization of science to reach engineering objectives.

Conversely, the long-established sectors are the ones where we find the greatest communication problem between the MSE professional and the traditional applications expert. If MSE is to make significant contributions in experience-intensive areas which are of prime importance to the economy, ways must be found to support technical advances with mechanisms for adequate transfer of new technologies across a broad front of applications.

Until recently much of the federal support for materials research and development in the United States came from the Department of Defense (DoD), the National Aeronautics and Space Administration (NASA), and the Atomic Energy Commission (AEC). These three agencies accounted for about 81% of the federal support for metallurgy and materials engineering in FY 1971. With regard to MSE, the three agencies had in common the pursuit of programs which were materials limited. For example, in the DoD, the development of infrared surveillance devices required semiconducting materials with higher quantum efficiency and lower noise. In the AEC, progress toward more efficient reactors required fuel elements for fast-neutron reactors. In NASA, adequate rocket performance demanded control-vane materials with high-temperature strength and oxidation resistance never before attained. This list of examples could be expanded almost indefinitely. In that technological environment, materials development was recognized as of central importance. Consequently, MSE has been supported extensively in the agencies' own laboratories, at universities and in relevant industries, both directly and indirectly.

The Committee on Materials (COMAT)* of the U. S. Federal Council for Science and Technology has recently made a broad survey of the materials research and development supported by all federal agencies [106]. Table 4 taken from that report shows the distribution of materials research and development funds related to function, *i.e.* the stage in the materials cycle, and by sponsoring agency. The entire materials cycle has been included by COMAT, whereas our review of MSE has tended to focus more on only portions of the materials cycle. The main differences appear in the functions: explorations for resources, extraction of raw materials, and waste management. In spite of such differences, the COMAT Report provides an excellent insight into the role which MSE is playing in the various societal goal-oriented programs. The distribution of materials research and development funds to national goals by participating federal agencies is displayed in Table 5 taken from the COMAT Report. It is clear that MSE is important in many programs.

On a first look, it appeared that some of the newer governmental agencies such as the Department of Housing and Urban Development and the Department of Transportation might not require the same proportion of MSE as have the defense, atomic energy, and space agencies. It is to be expected that such new agencies will first go through a phase of utilizing and applying existing knowledge. An example is the Bay Area Rapid Transit (BART) in the San Francisco area, the first underground transportation system designed since 1907. BART required little, if any, new materials development. Similarly, there is no one major materials impediment to the construction of wide scale, low cost urban housing. In the health area, the largest problems of the present time center about the provision and distribution of medical services rather than in limitations of any one materials-

related surgical procedure or treatment technique.

On a second look, the situation is not at all that simple. As mentioned, the first phase of the new programs can make significant contributions by utilizing existing technology, including materials. As time goes on, however, important needs become evident for further materials development and refinement. Indeed, we already find examples in the area of environmental quality and pollution. Internal combustion engines emit among other things undesirable oxides of nitrogen. A suitable catalyst could provide for the elimination of such a compound, but no thoroughly satisfactory catalyst is now available. It would appear that new approaches are required. A quite different way to avoid the emissions from internal combustion engines lies in the use of the electric batteries for vehicle power. There is some indication that batteries with solid electrolytes might overcome the classical difficulties of battery-operated automobiles. At the present time, materials are clearly the limitation to this approach. To take another case, the dangers of water pollution by mercury have been publicized in only the past several years. One possible solution toward the management of this low-level but toxic contaminant is through surface adsorption on solid particles; however the development of any practical, economic system awaits further understanding of surface states and the interaction of adsorbed particles with the substrate. These are but two examples to make the point that the newly emphasized societal programs definitely depend on contributions from MSE.

The changing agency base for governmental support in MSE has an important implication. The changing goals and programs forecast a broadening of emphasis within MSE from science toward engineering and application.

The balance between science and engineering has also changed during the past few years in the industrial sector. The technological trickle-down theory from scientific research, popular during the sixties, has met with skepticism. It is now felt that considerable engineering and applications-oriented effort must be expended directly on the problem in hand to produce significant results. Some companies consider that there is a backlog of scientific knowledge relevant to their

---

*Not to be confused with COSMAT.

TABLE 4

Distribution of materials research and development funds related to function (stage in materials cycle) by U. S. sponsoring agency ($1000) [106]

U. S. Agency	Exploration for resources	Extraction of raw materials	Processing of raw materials	Manufacture and fabrication	Application and utilization	Evaluation of properties	Development of materials	Waste management	Unspecified	Total
Department of Commerce	—	—	72	708	3812	7194	1979	151	7164	21 080
Department of Defense	—	—	184	2776	29 390	25 410	57 373	60	16 688	131 881
Department of Interior	38 308	80 908	16 100	375	2584	900	845	14 105	11 225	165 350
Environmental Protection Agency	—	2879	4116	5187	2017	62 394	—	21 332	1474	99 399
Energy Research and Development Administration	14 000	152	30 420	3240	124 658	69 089	7075	45 485	38 778	332 897
National Aeronautics and Space Administration	2324	—	—	—	26	11 117	37 639	—	427	51 533
National Science Foundation	4800	—	600	690	8000	19 305	2680	6100	26 525	68 700
Department of Agriculture	11	5064	8875	3070	8576	601	4208	4321	3528	38 254
Other Agencies	505	80	130	198	8520	23 478	10 979	2320	6016	52 226
Totals	59 948	89 083	60 497	16 244	187 583	219 488	122 778	93 874	111 825	961 320
Percent[a]	7.0	10.5	7.1	1.9	22.1	25.8	14.5	11.1	—	100.0

[a]Excluding "unspecified".

TABLE 5

Distribution of materials research and development funds sponsored by participating U.S. federal agencies in support of national goals ($1000) [106]

U. S. Agency	National Goal							
	National security	Materials supplies	Energy	Standards of living	Environment	Transportation	Communication	Science and technology
Department of Commerce	–	–	1993	1495	918	5430	–	5292
Department of Defense	131 663	–	2245	40	–	–	929	7521
Department of Interior	–	59 429	94 816	31 295	18 337	200	–	16 158
Environmental Protection Agency	–	989	12 319	35 218	68 775	–	–	–
Energy Research and Development Administration	58 800	14 573	194 203	750	26 622	–	875	12 726
National Aeronautics and Space Administration	277	2324	350	–	–	9437	–	11 401
Department of Agriculture	–	469	3180	2477	7893	6	–	186
Other agencies	132	17 133	11 816	30 484	6875	6078	994	46 515
Totals	190 872	94 917	320 922	101 759	129 420	21 151	2798	99 799

Totals are not additive; funds may be attributed to more than one goal where appropriate.

business and that they must now spend proportionately more of their resources in applying this knowledge. The economic recession of 1971 in the United States induced a retrenchment from scientific research to applications engineering in many companies. That retrenchment has not been significantly reversed even though many companies, particularly in the experience-based industries, could benefit from more science involvement in their development and production programs.

In the societal goals such as transportation, housing and environmental quality, while there are materials problems to be solved, there are also many other impediments. Substantial gains can be obtained through a systematic engineering application of knowledge which is already available in some form. Therefore, the MSE contribution in these new areas will, for the near term, be more engineering than scientific in character.

We are discussing here only a change in emphasis between science and engineering and by no means an elimination of the scientific portion of MSE. The big three* agencies in the United States continue to support materials research at a high level. The nature of their objectives requires the continued expansion of materials-science knowledge. Even for the newer societal goals, the demand for additional scientific understanding will rise as the existing relevant knowledge is applied in the early engineering accomplishments.

The more recent federal agencies such as the Department of Transportation, the Department of Housing and Urban Development, and the Environmental Protection Agency do not have a long tradition of working with materials professionals. Program managers in the agencies may not be aware of the potential contributions of MSE. The MSE community should take the initiative in closing this gap.

Opportunities for Materials Science and Engineering in Some Areas of Concern to Society

We have already shown how MSE has been responsive to societal needs when these have been clearly expressed and adequately funded. Materials requirements for new military technology, for exploitation of nuclear energy,

---

*Defense, Energy and NASA.

and for the conquests of space have been answered by important contributions in the interdisciplinary mode of MSE. Major industrial advances and creation of new industries, described elsewhere in this paper, have resulted directly from contributions in MSE. However, when viewed from today's perspective, the materials community might be criticized for not having given adequate attention in the past to certain elements of the materials cycle such as pollution and recycling; but all the evidence indicates that MSE will respond as new goals are defined and requirements spelled out. It is appropriate to comment briefly on such areas.

Resources, substitutions and synthesis

Resources, substitutions and synthesis set a perspective for material availability over the next several decades. We are not concerned here with a detailed projection for planning purposes. Rather, the point with respect to MSE is that, with sufficient planning and effort, we can have adequate resources for the foreseeable future. In order to accomplish this, substitution at several levels will be required. This is precisely where MSE will play a central role. First, one material can be directly substituted for another. The example of potentially substituting aluminum for copper was discussed earlier. Secondly, one can substitute a different function for one which is limited by scarce materials. An illustration is the use of microwave links or glass fibers to avoid long runs of copper-containing cable. At the third level, substitution may take the form of an entirely new technology, such as generation of electrical power by nuclear reactors to supersede fossil-fuel generators. In many cases, the development of adequate substitutes will require synthesis of new materials, which is precisely the arena where MSE plays a dominant role.

Materials for housing and urban renewal

While materials development can make important contributions to this national goal, the principal roadblocks lie in the nature of the industry, the inertia of building codes and the requirements for long-life performance. Perhaps MSE can have its greatest leverage on materials development for housing construction through the creation of a materials review board of truly national scope and prestige in order to provide a critical and impartial evaluation of new materials sufficent to establish confidence in the minds of the architect, the builder and the customer. Without doubt, science and engineering must couple closely to develop a knowledge-base on which to predict materials performance for periods as long as 50 years. Similarly, MSE can also make a significant contribution by helping to provide scientifically based fire standards and fire-testing procedures for materials of construction.

Environmental quality

Environmental quality is a goal toward which MSE should play a pivotal role. Although much can be accomplished by better exploitations of known engineering practices, ultimately a much larger science base will be required for the optimal control of environmental quality. Purposeful coupling of science and engineering in MSE can effectively aid in the solution of a number of major problems such as pollution, recycling, manufacturing process efficiency, and instrumentation to measure environmental degradation.

Materials science and engineering in medicine and biology

With a few important exceptions, the medical profession has done what it could on implanted prostheses using materials which had been evolved for other purposes. Recent development of new materials accomplished by close cooperation between materials specialists and medical practitioners has highlighted the progress which can be made in this field. Such instances afford excellent illustrations of the interdisciplinary nature of this activity, the need for additional scientific understanding and the opportunities for new modes of interaction between the materials community and medical science.

Energy

The importance of an inexpensive energy supply, particularly to industrial nations, has been dramatized in the past few years. Limitations on petroleum sources have brought about intensive efforts on a broad range of energy technologies. Virtually all of the new technologies involve processing in some form, which in turn requires materials with special performance characteristics. Coal must now be cleaned by solvent refining or by stack

scrubbing, or else converted to liquid or gaseous fuels. Solar energy puts emphasis on long-life reflecting or absorbing surfaces and on novel thermal-storage schemes. Geothermal sources involve high temperature, extremely corrosive fluids. Electric generators of higher efficiency also demand materials which will survive very high temperature, corrosive environments for long times. Batteries for load leveling or transportation must be based on advanced materials systems to achieve the required specific energy density and cycle life. These are only a few examples of the many which could be cited in the energy field where the program depends in a critical way on materials development of the type which has been successfully handled by the interdisciplinary MSE approach.

This brief list of societal goals is in no sense complete, but it is sufficient to demonstrate that major national goals can be readily identified for which MSE must respond in vital ways.

Diffusion of materials science and engineering into low technology industries

Coupling from an established field to an emerging activity is an important facet of MSE. Wood products serve as a good example. Until recently, structural wood was kiln dried, inspected by visual criteria and utlized with large safety factors to offset the wide variation from board to board. The concepts of solid-state MSE are now being reviewed for application to the problem. One of the newest developments to improve the engineering properties of wood is a special application of non-destructive testing (NDT). Whereas NDT is usually applied to other materials in order to detect unwanted inclusions or discontinuities, in wood it is being adopted to measure physical properties. For this purpose, various mechanical and electronic devices are employed to measure deflections and loads, or to monitor vibrations, in order to determine the modulus of elasticity. From such testing, other strength properties such as modulus of rupture are estimated through correlative procedures. Thus, the stronger pieces can be identified and although the properties have not been modified in any particular way, the engineer can now select a superior material to design more efficient load-carrying structures. Overtones of effective conservation are evident in the practice of NDT methods.

However, it has been found that correlative procedures for estimated strength properties from modulus of elasticity are not sufficiently precise for some critical engineering applications, such as for the chord members of trusses or the bottom members of laminated beams. Hence, there is continuing effort to improve NDT techniques. One possibility in this direction is based on the theory that energy dissipation or internal friction may be related to the same mechanism that controls strength properties. Fundamental studies in this field involve fracture mechanics, stress-wave theory, mathematical modeling, physics and basic wood structure.

Materials Science and Engineering and the Broader Scene

In the final analysis, MSE may fail even though it is properly organized as an interdisciplinary team and staffed with individuals of proper training and experience. Difficulty may well arise in the acceptance of new materials. Such obstacles may be due to human qualities, such as habit or inertia, or to organizational barriers which impede change and progress. In emerging programs, where there is generally high enthusiasm to develop something new, the requirement for materials development is more often recognized, and materials contributions are accepted because the success of the program is seen to demand their acceptance.

In mature industries, however, the situation may be quite different. Long-known materials and processes are familiar and comfortable; new materials may seem threatening because they introduce unknown technical risks. In industries where the material itself is directly observable by the customer, there is also much reluctance to adopt different materials. The shoddy ersatz materials necessitated by World War II shortages sensitized the public adversely to material substitutions. Fortunately, the outstanding successes of a wide variety of plastic materials with superior characteristics have offset this suspicion to the extent that many products are now accepted more quickly. Industry-wide self-discipline with regard to releasing new materials should also help eliminate this long-standing public prejudice against substitute materials.

Until now, MSE has contributed to national well-being mainly by technical proficiency. It is time to recognize that the role of MSE in new national goals will require more than elegant solutions of technical problems. Also important are related factors in the realm of social science due to problems arising from long-held customs, threat of change, questioning of something new, and difficulties in communication of semitechnical information to the public. Thus, MSE must learn how to join forces with social research in order to meet its larger objectives. Some effort along these lines has been started in governmental laboratories and industrial concerns, but the university would appear to be an ideal location for this type of broad interdisciplinary activity.

REFERENCES

1 The most popular — and most terrifying — of the projections prophesying dire results of the current trends in materials use in relation to present rates of population growth is to be found in the report of the Club of Rome's Project on the Predicament of Mankind. See D. H. Meadows, D. L. Meadows, J. Randers and W. W. W. Behrens, III, The Limits to Growth, Universe Books, New York, 1972. The Club of Rome has since modified some of the doomsday conclusions of The Limits to Growth study; see G. Pestel and M. Mesarovic, Mankind at the Turning Point, New American Library, New York, 1976.

2 Sir George P. Thomson, "... a New Materials Age", General Electric Forum XI, Vol. 1, Summer 1965, p. 5.

3 This is one of the major theses of A. Toffler, Future Shock, Random House, New York, 1970.

4 There is a formidable literature of anti-science and anti-technology. Not only are there the attacks of the counter-culture (represented by the writings of T. Roszak, P. Goodman and H. Marcuse), but more thoughtful observers, such as L. Mumford, have attacked the spirit and practice of science and technology in the modern world. Among scientists, the work of B. Commoner (The Closing Circle, Knopf, New York, 1971) stands out in this regard. However, a more constructive evaluation of technology is emerging in such works as: R. Prisig, Zen and the Art of Motorcycle Maintenance, Bantam, Des Plaines, III., 1976; A. Pacey, The Maze of Ingenuity, Holmes and Meier, New York, 1975; S. C. Florman, The Existential Pleasures of Engineering, St. Martin's, New York, 1976.

5 Oeconomicus, Book IV; see also Sir Desmond Lee, Science, Technology and Philosophy in the Greco-Roman World, Greece and Rome, 20 (1973) 70, 71.

6 Th. Dobzhansky, Mankind Evolving: The Evolution of the Human Species, Yale University Press, New Haven, 1962. A popular account is to be found in J. E. Pfeiffer, The Emergence of Man, Harper and Row, New York, 1972.

7 See V. G. Childe, Man Makes Himself, Mentor, New York, 1951, Chaps. 1, 2; What Happened in History, Penguin, New York, 1946, Chap. 1.

8 See S. L. Washburn, Speculations on the Interrelations of the History of Tools and Biological Evolution. In J. N. Spuhler, (ed.), The Evolution of Man's Capacity for Culture, Wayne University Press, Detroit, 1959, pp. 21 - 31. A. Brues, The Spearman and the Archer — An Essay on Selection in Body Build, Am. Anthropol., 61 (1959) 457 - 469. See also The Dawn of Civilization, McGraw-Hill, New York, 1961.

9 R. F. Heizer, The background of Thomson's three-age system, Technol. Cult., 3 (Summer 1962) 259 - 266.

10 J. Jacobs, The Economy of Cities, Random House, New York, 1969.

11 C. Levi-Strauss, The Raw and the Cooked: Introduction to a Science of Mythology, Harper and Row, New York, 1969.

12 W. H. Gourdin and W. H. Kingery, The Beginnings of pyrotechnology: neolithic and egyptian lime plaster, J. Field Archaeology, 2 (1975) 133 - 150.

13 J. F. Epstein, Flint Technology and the Heating of Stone. In D. Schmandt-Besserat (ed.), Early Technologies (Proc. Symposium at University of Texas, October, 1976.

14 D. Schmandt-Besserat, Ochre in prehistory. In J. D. Muhly and T. A. Wertime (eds.), The Coming of the Age of Iron, in the press.

15 C. S. Smith, Art, technology and science: notes on their historical interaction, Technol. Cult., 11 (1970) 493 - 549; also published in D. H. D. Roller (ed.), Perspectives in the History of Science and Technology, University of Oklahoma Press, Norman, 1971, pp. 129 - 165.

16 W. Sullivan, Anthropologists urged to study existing stone-age cultures, New York Times, April 5, 1965. (Description of conference paper by J. D. Clark, University of California, Berkeley.)

17 K. P. Oakley, Man the Tool-maker, 6th edn., University of Chicago, Chicago, 1972, p. 81 ff.

18 V. G. Childe, What Happened in History, Penguin, New York, 1946.

19 R. F. Heizer, The background of Thomson's three-age system, Technol. Cult., 3 (1962) 259 - 266.

20 L. Aitchison, A History of Metals, Macdonald and Evans, London, 1960; Interscience Publishers, New York, 1960. This provides the background for much of the discussion of metals. See also T. A. Wertime, Man's first encounters with metallurgy, Science, 146 (3649) (December 4, 1964) 1257 - 1267; R. F. Tylecote, A History of

Metallurgy, Metals Society, London, 1976; and W. D. Muhly and T. A. Wertime (eds.), The Coming of the Age of Iron, in the press.

21 E. Eaton and H. McKerrel, Near eastern alloying and some textual evidence for the early use of arsenical copper, World Archeology, 8 (1976) 168 - 191.

22 C. Renfrew, The autonomy of the east european copper age, Proc. Prehistoric Soc., 35 (1969) 12 - 47.

23 K. A. Wittvogel, Oriental Despotism, Yale University Press, New Haven, 1957.

24 V. G. Childe, Rotary Motion. In C. Singer et al. (eds.), A History of Technology, Vol. I, Oxford University Press, New York and London, 1954, Chap. 1.

25 D. Schmandt-Besserat, An archaic recording system and the origin of writing, Syro–Mesopotamian Studies, I (1977) 31 - 70.

26 M. McLuhan, Understanding Media: The Extensions of Man, McFraw-Hill, New York, 1964.

27 R. J. Forbes, Extracting, smelting and alloying. In C. Singer et al. (eds.), A History of Technology, Vol. I, Chap. 21 (see also ref. 24).

28 R. Maddin et al., How the iron age began, Sci. Am., 237 (1977) 122 - 131; J. D. Muhly and T. A. Wertime (eds.), The Coming of the Age of Iron, in the press.

29 Samuel Lilley, Men, Machines and History, International Publishers, New York, 1966, pp. 9 - 12.

30 N. Davey, A History of Building Materials, Phoenix House, London, 1961. See also I. L. Znachko-Iavorskii, New methods for the study and contemporary aspects of the history of cementing materials, Technol. Cult., 18 (1977) 25 - 42.

31 C. S. Smith, Matter versus materials, a historical view, Science, 162 (1968) 637 - 644.

32 C. S. Smith, A History of Metallography, University of Chicago Press, 1960; Metallurgy as a human experience, Metall. Trans., 6A (1975) 603; reprinted as a separate booklet by Am. Soc. Metals, Metals Park, Ohio, 1977, and Am. Inst. Mech. Eng., New York, 1977.

33 S. C. Gilfillan, Roman culture and dysgenic lead poisoning, Mankind Q., 3 (January - March 1965) 3 - 20; see also S. C. Gilfillan, The Inventive lag in classical mediterranean society, Technol. Cult., 3 (1962) 85 - 87.

34 C. C. Patterson, Silver stocks and their half-lives in ancient and medieval times, Economic History Rev., 1972.

35 There have been two recent English translations of Theophilus, C. R. Dodwell, Thomas Nelson and Sons, London, 1961, and C. S. Smith and J. G. Hawthorne, University of Chicago Press, Chicago, 1963. The former contains an excellent edited version of the Latin text; the notes in the latter place more stress on technical aspects. For a further discussion, see L. White, Jr., Theophilus Redivivus, Technol. Cult., 5 (1964) 224 - 233.

36 L. White, Jr., Medieval Technology and Social Change, Oxford Univ. Press: Clarendon Press, Oxford, 1962.

37 H. R. Schubert, History of the British Iron and Steel Industry — to A.D. 1775, Routledge and Kegan Paul, London, 1957.

38 R. P. Multhauf, The Origins of Chemistry, Oldbourne, London, 1966; this provides an authoritative and lucid discussion of the development of chemical theory and practice and their relations to materials.

39 The standard work on the early history of printing is T. F. Carter, The Invention of Printing and Its Spread Westward, revised by L. Carrington Goodrich, 2nd edn., Ronald Press, New York, 1955. See also H. Carter, A View of Early Typography, Oxford University Press, Oxford, 1969.

40 A. R. Hall, Science, Technology and Warfare, 1400 - 1700. In M. D. Wright and L. J. Paszk (eds.), Science, Technology and Warfare, Office of Air Force History and United States Air Force Academy, U. S. Government Printing Office, Washington, D. C., 1970, pp. 3 - 24.

41 L. White, Jr., Medieval Technology and Social Change, Oxford Univ. Press, Oxford, 1962. See also L. White, Jr., Ballistics in the Seventeenth Century, Cambridge University Press, Cambridge, 1952.

42 An English translation of Agricola was published by H. C. Hoover and his wife L. H. Hoover, London, 1912, and was reprinted by Dover, New York, 1950. See also B. Dibner, Agricola on Metals, Burndy Library, Norwalk, Conn., 1958.

43 C. S. Smith and M. T. Gnudi, The Pirotechnia of Vannoccio Biringuccio, Am. Inst. Mech. Eng., New York, 1942; paperbound edition, MIT Press, Cambridge, Mass., 1966.

44 A. G. Sisco and C. S. Smith, Lazarus Ercker's Treatise on Ores and Assaying, University of Chicago Press, Chicago, Illinois, 1951.

45 R. A. F. de Réaumur, Memoirs on Steel and Iron, translated and edited by A. G. Sisco, University of Chicago Press, Chicago, Illinois, 1956.

46 W. Rozdzienski, Officina Ferraria, in W. Rózánski and C. S. Smith (eds.), Society for the History of Technology and MIT Press, Cambridge, Mass., 1976.

47 C. S. Smith (ed.), Sources for the History of Science and Steel, 1532 - 1786, MIT Press, Cambridge, Mass., 1968.

48 C. Piccolpasso, The Three Books of the Potter's Art, edited and translated by B. Racham and A. van de Put, London, 1934.

49 S. M. Edelstein and H. Borghetty (eds.), The Plitcho of Gioanventura Rosetti, MIT Press, Cambridge, Mass., 1969.

50 For a bibliography and analysis of these works, see J. Ferguson, Some Early Treatises of Technological Chemistry, Proc. Philos. Soc., Glasgow, 19 (1888) 126 - 159; 25 (1894) 224 - 235; 43 (1911) 232 - 258; 44 (1912) 149 - 189. See also E. Darmstaedter, Berg-Kunst- und Probierbuchlein, Münchner Drucke, Munich, 1926; and Sidney M. Edelstein, The Allerley Matkel, 1532, Technol. Cult., 5 (1964) 297 - 321.

51 E. Layton, Mirror-image twins: the communities of science and technology in 19th-century America, Technol. Cult., 12 (Oct. 1971) 562 - 580.

52 R. P. Multhauf, Sal ammoniac: a case history of industrialization, Technol. Cult., 6 (Fall 1965) 569 - 586.

53 This view has been challenged by A. E. Musson and E. Robinson, Science and Technology in the Industrial Revolution, University of Toronto Press, Toronto, 1969. However, a recent article by E. Ferguson, The mind's eye: nonverbal thought in technology, Science, 197 (1977) 827 - 836, convincingly emphasizes the central historical importance of the practitioner's feeling for the way things work and of the necessity of making final choices by processes more akin to art than to calculation.

54 L. Bryant, A Little Learning. In Karl-Heinz Manegold (ed.), Wissenschaft, Wirtschaft, und Technik, F. Bruckmann, Munich, 1969; a revised version, The role of thermodynamics in the evolution of heat engines, appears in Technol. Cult., 14 (April 1973) 153 - 165.

55 Some discussion of the role of plating in the beginning of the electric power industry will be found in C. S. Smith, Reflections on technology and the decorative arts in the nineteenth century. In I. M. G. Quimby and P. A. Earl (eds.), Technological Innovation and the Decorative Arts, University of Virginia Press, Charlottesville, Va., 1974, pp. 1 - 62.

56 C. S. Smith, The discovery of carbon in steel, Technol. Cult., 5 (1964) 149 - 175; see also ref. 47.

57 See A. G. Sisco, Réaumur's Memoirs on Steel and Iron, ref. 45.

58 C. S. Smith (ed.), The Sorby Centennial Symposium on the History of Metallurgy, Gordon and Breach, New York, 1965; see also ref. 32.

59 H. R. Schubert, History of the British Iron and Steel Industry — to A.D. 1775, Routledge and Kegan Paul, London, 1957.
T. A. Wertime, The Coming of the Age of Steel, University of Chicago Press, Chicago, 1962.
L. Beck, Geschichte des Eisens in seiner technische und kulturgeschichtlichen Beziehung, Brunswick, 1891 - 1903.
O. Johannsen, Geschichte des Eisens, 3rd edn., Dusseldorf, 1953; an English translation has been published.

60 E. E. Morison, Men, Machines and Modern Times, MIT Press, Cambridge, Mass., 1966.

61 H. Bessemer, An Autobiography, Offices of Engineering, London, 1905.

62 H. Y. Hunsicker and H. C. Stumpf, History of precipitation hardening, in Sorby Centennial Symposium on the History of Metallurgy, Gordon and Breach, New York, 1965, pp. 271 - 311.

63 J. D. Bernal, Science and Industry in the Nineteenth Century, Routledge and Kegan Paul, London, 1953, pp. 181 - 219.

64 M. P. Crosland, Historical Studies in the Language of Chemistry, Harvard University Press, Cambridge, Mass., 1962.

65 J. J. Beer, The Emergence of the German Dye Industry, University of Illinois Press, Urbana, Illinois, 1959.

66 M. Kaufman, The First Century of Plastics, The Plastics Institute, London, 1963.

67 J. G. Burke, The Origins of the Science of Crystals, University of California Press, Berkeley, 1966.

68 P. P. Ewald et al., Fifty Years of X-Ray Diffraction, International Union of Crystallography, Utrecht, 1962.

69 S. P. Timoshenko, History of Strength of Materials with a Brief Account of the History of Theory of Elasticity and Theory of Structures, McGraw-Hill, New York, 1953.
I. Todhunter and K. Pearson, History of the Theory of Elasticity and Strength of Materials, London, 1886 - 1893.

70 J. G. Burke, Bursting boilers and the federal power, Technol. Cult., 7 (1966) 1 - 23.

71 Report of the United States Board Appointed to Test Iron, Steel and Other Metals, Government Printing Office, Washington D. C., 1881.

72 E. Layton, Mirror-image twins: the communities of science and technology in 19th century America, Technol. Cult., 12 (Oct. 1971) 1 - 26.

73 For a review of the relations between science and technology, see the series of articles by M. Kranzberg, The Unity of Science–Technology, Am. Sci., 55 (March 1967) 48 - 66; The Disunity of Science–Technology, Am. Sci., 56 (Spring 1968) 21 - 34; The Spectrum of Science–Technology, J. Sci. Lab., 48 (Dec. 1967) 47 - 58. See also The Interaction of Science and Technology in the Industrial Age, In Nathan Reingold and Arthur Molella (eds.), Technol. Cult., (1976) 621 - 742.

74 R. W. Douglas and S. Frank, A History of Glassmaking, G. T. Foulis and Co., Henly-on-Thames, 1972.

75 C. S. Smith, Matter versus materials, a historical view, Science, 162 (1968) 643.

76 This environmentalist view is expanded in C. S. Smith, Hierarchical structure in art and science. In J. Wechsler (ed.), Aesthetics in Science, Cambridge, Mass., 1978, pp. 9 - 53.

77 W. D. Lewis, Industrial Research and Development. In M. Kranzberg and C. W. Pursell, Jr. (eds.), Technology in Western Civilization, Oxford Univ. Press, New York, 1967, Vol. II, Chap. 40.

78 W. D. Rasmussen, Scientific Agriculture. In M. Kranzberg and C. W. Pursell (eds.), Technology in in Western Civilization, Oxford Univ. Press, New York, Vol. II, Chap. 22.

79 L. Hoddeson, The Roots of Solid State Research at Bell Labs., Phys. Today, 30 (3) (1977) 23 - 30.
C. Weiner, How the Transistor Emerged, IEEE Spectrum, 10 (Jan. 1973). G. L. Pearson and W. H. Brattain, History of Semiconductor Research, Proc. Inst. Radio Eng., 43 (1955) 1794 - 1806.

80 W. Hume-Rothery, The Development of the Theory of Alloys. In C. S. Smith (ed.), Sorby Centennial Symposium on the History of Metallurgy, Gordon and Breach, New York, 1965, pp. 331 - 346.

81 R. Roy (ed.), Materials Science and Engineering in the United States, Pennsylvania State University Press, University Park, Pa., 1970, p. 117.

82 P. F. Drucker, Technological Trends in the 20th Century. In M. Kranzberg and C. W. Pursell, (eds.), Technology in Western Civilization, Oxford Univ. Press, New York, 1967, Vol. II, Chap. 2.

83 H. R. Clauser, Materials Effectiveness, Materials Engineering, and National Materials Policy. In Problems and Issues of a National Materials Policy, Committee Print, Committee on Public Works, U. S. Senate, 91st Congress, 2nd session, Washington, 1970, p. 178. This document, consisting of papers presented at the Engineering Foundation Research Conference on National Materials Policy, July, 1970, contains a number of papers which have been helpful in preparing this section.

84 See ref. 79.

85 R. Hadfield, Metallurgy and Its Influence on Modern Progress, Chapman and Hall, London, 1925. On transformer iron, see especially pp. 125 - 139. See also J. H. Bechtold and G. W. Wiener, The History of Soft-Magnetic Materials. In C. S. Smith (ed.), Sorby Centennial Symposium, pp. 501 - 518. (See ref. 47.)

86 Materials and Man's Needs, Materials Science and Engineering, COSMAT Summary Report of the Committee on the Survey of Materials Science and Engineering, Washington, D.C., NAS, 1974.

87 American Science Manpower 1968, A Report of the National Register of Scientific and Technical Personnel, NSF 69-38, Appendix C, 1969, p. 265.

88 Statistics from the 1969 National Engineers Register, New York, 1970.

89 Final Report of the National Commission on Materials Policy, 1973, Superintendent of Documents, U. S. GPO Report 06224, 1974.

90 J. H. Sinfelt, Polymetallic Cluster Catalysts, Platinum Met. Rev., 20 (1976) 114.

91 S. H. Bush, Structural Materials for Nuclear Power Plants, J. Test. Eval., 2 (6) (1974) 435.

92 R. S. Nelson, Void Formation in Fast-Reactor Materials, Int. Metall. Rev., 19 (1974) 247.

93 W. E. Keller, Application of superconductivity to electrical power equipment, Elec. Power Syst. Res., 1 (1977 - 1978) 21.

94 H. L. Lagner, J. W. Dean and P. Chaowdhuri, Electrical, cryogenic and system design of a d.c. superconducting transmission line, IEEE Trans. Magn., MAG-13 (1977) 182.

95 E. W. Schmidt, Thermochemical Energy Storage Systems, 11th Intersoc. Energy Conv. Eng. Conf. I (1976) 665.

96 H. W. Prengle, Jr., and C. H. Sun, Operational chemical storage cycles for utilization of solar energy to produce heat or electric power, Sol. Energy, 18 (1976) 561.

97 K. H. Hegemann and M. C. Larkin, The steel industry and its response to the environmental control challenge, Steel Times, 205 (11) (1977) 57.

98 A. G. Chynoweth, Fiber lightguides for optical communications, Mater. Sci. Eng., 25 (1976) 5.

99 A study of success and failure in innovation, Sappho Report, Univ. of Sussex, England; Sci. Pol. Res. Unit, 1971.

100 Webster's Third New International Dictionary, Merriam Co., Springfield, Mass., 1967, p. 611.

101 S. Stickler, Microstructure of nickel base superalloys, Phys. Status Solidi, 35 (1969) 11.

102 Organization for Economic Cooperation and Development Report on Problems and Prospects of Fundamental Research in Selected Scientific Fields — Materials, OECD, 1972.

103 Principles of Research — Engineering Interaction, Report of the Ad Hoc Committee, Washington, D. C., MAB-222-M, NAS-NRC, 1966.

104 G. J. Knezo, Report prepared for the Subcommittee on Science, Research and Development of the Committee on Science and Astronautics, U. S. House of Rep., Science Policy Res. Div., Leg. Ref. Serv., Library of Congress, Oct. 30, 1970.

105 SSLA, Ekonomike, Politika, Ideologiga, April 1971.

106 Inventory and Analysis of Materials Life Cycle Research and Development, Phase 1 Rep.; Federal Govt.: COMAT Task Force 1, Fiscal Year 1976, April 1976.